APRS

Moving Hams on Radio and the Internet

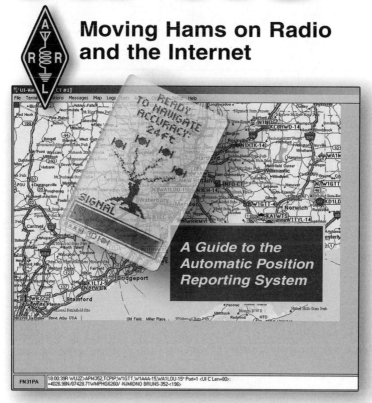

A Guide to the Automatic Position Reporting System

by Stan Horzepa, WA1LOU

Published by:

ARRL *The national association for AMATEUR RADIO*

225 Main Street • Newington, CT 06111-1494 USA

ARRLWeb: **www.arrl.org/**

CONTENTS

FOREWORD

Bob Bruninga, WB4APR, the "father of APRS," graciously agreed to write the Foreword of this book.

Although APRS (Automatic Positioning Reporting System) is now passing its 10-year anniversary since it was first introduced by name at the ARRL and TAPR Digital Communications Conference in 1992, its roots go back to the beginning of amateur packet radio in the late 1970s.

From the first days of packet radio, hams had the ability for group discussions with everyone sharing in the round-table exchange of packets. Nevertheless, this capability was soon lost to most operators in the evolution towards packet bulletin boards and e-mail, which predominated in the 1980s and early 90s. Such point-to-point data exchanges were ignoring the vast number of ham radio applications that are not point-to-point, but consist of nets where a large number of people share in a common exchange of information contributed by many individuals.

To keep the multi-user network concept alive during that timeframe, I had begun experimenting with APRS-like connectionless multi-user networks running on the VIC-20 and Commodore C-64 computers to serve the needs of special events and emergencies. That was the fundamental basis of APRS dating back to 1985.

APRS is a common local network for the exchange of whatever data is of local interest. It is *not* a vehicle location system as so many people try to make it. It is also not a 24 hour-a-day, 7 day-a-week long distance communication network of boring, unchanging, non-moving, repetitive data.

APRS is supposed to be a come-as-you-are instantaneous means of exchanging data (any data of short, but immediate interest) with everyone in range. APRS should work out-of-the-box with no prior local knowledge of any network parameters. It should work anywhere at anytime to establish communications between any users on the air. Such power and flexibility lays the groundwork for very broad application in ham radio.

With this broad foundation and on this tenth anniversary of APRS, there are two important points I think must be reiterated with respect to the future of APRS. Everyone with a wireless cell phone or pocket computer knows how there seems to be an almost infinite appetite for more wireless applications all of which require more bandwidth. These two words, applications and bandwidth, are the cornerstones that must guide us into the next decade.

Bandwidth

Some say that APRS is saturated. This is wrong thinking. In the 1960s, the mobile phone system was totally saturated until the birth of the cellular concept that allowed for multiple re-use of frequencies. The explosion of cellular technology and almost endless bandwidth for millions of subscribers is founded on the simple principle that expands bandwidth by simply making the cells smaller.

APRS is founded on the identical concept. APRS also has unlimited growth potential by just making the "cells" smaller. To most hams familiar with repeaters and digipeaters, the concept of making their ranges less, using lower towers and giving up mountaintop locations is repugnant to the past ways of thinking. Nevertheless, it is the only way to go forward.

When APRS was joined to the Internet by the efforts of Steve Dimse, K4HG, in the later 1990s, its global reach became inevitable. Today, APRS can penetrate anywhere on the globe through the combination of the ubiquitous IGates (Internet Gateways) and more recently, the presence of APRS digipeaters in space (PCsat, UO-22 and aboard the International Space Station [ISS]).

The availability of almost infinite bandwidth for "free" on the Internet, fiber, or backbones has made a paradigm shift that most ham operators have not awakened to yet; i.e., that the mountaintop microwave or repeater sites are dinosaurs and are not only worthless, but a liability.

A mountaintop or very tall microwave tower these days sees too much "spectrum," making it almost useless. Recently, American Tower, which owns over 2000 excess microwave relay sites, is auctioning them off at fire sale prices because they simply have *no* value in today's *fiber* backboned *wireless* environment. There is no economic value to owning a microwave relay site, high-maintenance tower and emergency power system just to use a few megahertz of a single microwave channel when a single optical fiber can carry hundreds of gigahertz of bandwidth and carry it further than every existing microwave tower in the state!

Similarly, as APRS grows in an area, its early, high digipeater sites become liabilities, which hold back bandwidth instead of being an asset. It is time for the local APRS operators to wake up to the fact that the local APRS RF channel should only be optimized for end-user access and should not be used for any long-haul transportation of data. We must begin to evolve our *high* digipeater sites to long-haul backbones and move that data off the user access channel to allow for growth.

Applications

The second key point that is missed by most newcomers to APRS is the wide possibilities of applications that are usually overlooked by everyone's fascination with the mobile vehicle location aspect of APRS.

APRS was never designed to be an automatic vehicle location system (AVLS). APRS is a local data network for exchange of *any* data that is of immediate need to the hams in range. Of course, the advent of GPS (Global Positioning System) made vehicle tracking a perfect application for APRS, but AVLS is not the driver of the APRS protocol, network or its potential applications.

Before GPS, the fundamental ham radio interest in position information and *maps* were easily summarized into four broad categories: DX contacts, direction finding (DFing), weather reporting, and, of course, the usual where-are-you report. Similarly, from the beginning, APRS not only fully supported all of these facets of Amateur Radio and gave the operator a mapping tool to be able to manipulate, display, and exchange every aspect of data regarding these important Amateur Radio missions, but as an integrated mapping system, APRS could offer a bold new capability to direction finding.

Using signal strength alone (no special DFing equipment), APRS can use its knowledge of position, antenna range and map data to localize the source of any signal within seconds. In addition, since most reporting stations often do not hear the signal directly, the ability of APRS to plot all of the areas where the signal is *not* detectible is actually a tremendous asset in localizing its source.

We need more education of APRS users and new authors to begin to look past the simple moving map displays of moving vehicles and apply the potential power of APRS to all the other applications we enjoy so much in *ham* radio. DFing with signal strength alone is one of those!

Another perfect marriage of the APRS data network to the new ham radio is in the exchange of data regarding the many *voice-over-Internet* connections being made to extend the range of radio. APRS is the end-user signaling system that can make available on the front panel of the user's radio all the information he needs to know about the *voice* system. Not only can he see the network and node status, but he should also be able to set up a point-to-point end user call via these global systems by simply entering the call sign of the called party into his APRS radio.

As we educate new users to the potential of APRS, as the end-user delivery mechanism of tiny-Web-pages of data to the front panel of radios or to palm-top computers for instant viewing and/or action, we will begin to see continuing explosive growth of APRS. As you enter the world of APRS, do not be limited in your imagination to the potential of APRS by the most obvious application of mobile vehicle position reporting. APRS is much, much more.

Bob Bruninga, WB4APR

DEDICATION

To my Uncle Wally, a good godfather.

1

INTRODUCTION

This chapter briefly describes how APRS works and what you can do with it after you get it up and running.

Since the publication of my previous book, *APRS: Tracks, Maps and Mobiles*, in 1999, APRS has evolved dramatically. For example, in 1999, there were six APRS applications. Today, there are nearly two dozen APRS applications.

The increase in the number of applications is not the biggest change in APRS. In 1999, Steve Dimse, K4HG, introduced the first APRS interface to the Internet and with that, the emphasis of APRS began to change significantly.

Today, instead of being just an RF (radio frequency) application, APRS is so intertwined with the Internet that its Internet interface is as important as its RF interface. As a result, this book has more emphasis on the Internet aspects of APRS than my previous APRS books. This book's title, *APRS: Moving Hams on Radio and the Internet*, reflects this increased emphasis.

When the ARRL published my previous APRS book, anyone with a computer, APRS software, TNC (terminal node controller) and receiver that covered the APRS frequencies, could experience APRS; ie, they could monitor the activity of APRS-equipped stations. However, the likelihood that anyone would have the requisite hardware and software to monitor APRS was next to nil unless they were a ham radio operator or radio hobbyist.

Today, anyone with access to a computer that is interfaced to the Internet can monitor APRS activity. You do not need a TNC, you do not need a receiver, and you do not even need APRS software to do it. As a result, the world of APRS is open to virtually everyone. For example, when I make my annual 735-mile trek to the Dayton Hamvention in Ohio, my family monitors my progress across four states via the Internet. No one in my extended family is a licensed ham, some have not even heard of APRS, yet they can experience ham radio in a very useful way.

However, I am getting ahead of myself. I am so involved with APRS that I assume that everyone in Amateur Radio knows what APRS is all about, but invariably, when I write something about APRS, I receive complaints that indicate that some of my readers do not know much about the mode beyond its acronym.

WHAT IS APRS?

APRS is an acronym for Automatic Position Reporting System. It integrates hardware and software to permit Amateur Radio operators to quickly disseminate data concerning real-time events and to graphically represent that data on their computers.

The system uses packet radio as the means of disseminating the data. In traditional packet radio operations, communications occurs on a one-to-one basis using connected packets, ie, two stations are virtually connected to each other. In APRS, stations use unconnected packets to disseminate data on a one-to-all basis, thus, expanding the audience to all the stations that can receive the APRS packets not just the single station that is virtually connected to the transmitting station. APRS uses the "beacon" function of traditional packet radio to accomplish this mode of communications.

The content of an APRS beacon packet is the key that changes a plain vanilla beacon packet into an APRS packet. Typically, an APRS packet contains station location (latitude and longitude) and station type (homes, portables, mobiles, digipeaters, weather stations, etc) information in a specific format that allows the APRS software running at receiving APRS stations to process the information contained therein, and display an appropriate symbol on a map showing the location of the beaconing station. If an APRS station such as a mobile or portable station is in motion, APRS changes the position of that station on the map when it receives a new position packet that indicates a change of location.

The station in motion may consist of a radio, TNC, and laptop computer running APRS. As that station travels along its route, the station operator updates the position of the station on the APRS map and APRS relays the new position to other APRS stations to update the position of the station on their APRS maps.

More likely, the station in motion consists of a radio, TNC, and a Global Positioning System (GPS) receiver, which receives signals from Earth-orbiting satellites to automatically calculate its location. The GPS receiver constantly sends position information to the TNC of the station in motion, which relays it to other APRS stations in order to update the position of the moving station on their APRS maps.

In addition to tracking stations in motion, APRS also tracks any object in motion when the position of that object is entered into the system. For example, you can enter the latitude and longitude of a hurricane and the position of the hurricane appears on the map of

Global Positioning System (GPS) satellites transmit signals that GPS receivers can use to calculate your position anywhere on the globe.

everyone using APRS on that channel. In that weather application, you can also interface weather-monitoring equipment to an APRS station to disseminate real-time weather information to other APRS stations.

Just like traditional packet radio stations, APRS stations use digipeaters ("APRS digis") to propagate their transmissions, but unlike traditional packet, APRS stations do not have to specify a digipeater path. Rather, APRS, stations use generic digipeater paths so that no prior knowledge of the network is needed. The generic path works whether you are in New York, New Delhi, Newcastle, or Newington.

To propagate APRS to the world, there are APRS stations that function as IGates (Internet gateways) that relay received APRS packets to servers connected to the Internet. These servers collect and disseminate current APRS data on an international and real-time basis via a variety of World Wide Web (www) pages, thus permitting anyone with a *Java*-capable Web browser to view APRS activity.

WHY APRS?

Now you know the basics of how APRS works, but you may ask, "What is the point? Why bother using Amateur Radio to track anything?"

Place an APRS station in an emergency vehicle being used in a disaster area or in the lead car of a parade, and the possibility of using APRS as a public service tool for tactical communications becomes obvious.

POSITION REPORTING

In response to the events of September 11, 2001, the Air Force tested the public service utility of APRS. The Rome Research Site of the Air Force Research Lab in upstate New York conducted an experiment using Amateur Radio operators to locate aircraft in trouble. The plan for the experiment was simple, but effective. Fly an airplane with an APRS station on-board, start transmitting APRS emergency beacons on the national APRS 2-meter frequency (144.39 MHz) and see if anyone responds.

The objective of the Precision Emergency Automated Position Reporting System (PEAPRS) test was to measure the timeliness and accuracy of the reports received from the Amateur Radio community. If successful, PEAPRS could provide the initial alert and position information of an aircraft in distress by taking advantage of the Amateur Radio operators monitoring the international APRS network. In a real life situation, a panic button, power loss, loss of cabin pressure, other on-board sensors, or ground interrogation could trigger the distress signal.

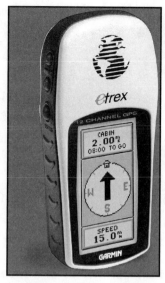

A typical GPS receiver.

The experiment was not a complete surprise. Announcements were broadcast two weeks beforehand on various Amateur Radio channels indicating when the experiment would occur and that the aircraft "in distress" would transmit emergency beacons using a specific call sign, but the date and time of the tests was not revealed. Stations receiving the emergency beacons e-mailed or phoned in their reception reports.

There were two test flights lasting approximately 20 minutes and 40 minutes each. The flight paths were over the northern portion of upstate New York at 35,000 to 45,000 feet. At that altitude, hams in New York, New England and Quebec were able to receive the emergency beacons directly and countless other hams beyond the direct coverage of the aircraft were able to receive reports via APRS digipeaters and the APRS interface on the Internet. Approximately 290 reports were received split evenly between the two flights.

PEAPRS is just one possible public service application of APRS. It is just the tip of the iceberg of APRS's public service utility. If tracking a moving object (even a moving object like an iceberg) can help save lives, then the potential exists for APRS to accomplish the task.

WEATHER REPORTING

Weather reporting has also become a very important aspect of

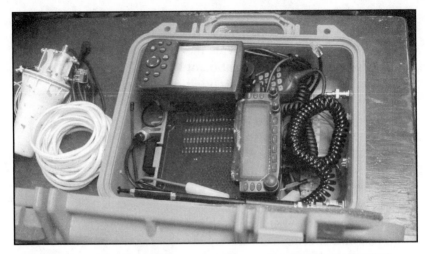

A portable APRS system in a waterproof case. Note the FM transceiver and GPS receiver.

APRS. Hams have interfaced their home weather stations to their home APRS stations to disseminate weather information over the APRS network.

These weather reports are so important that various agencies now collect the APRS weather information and use the information to provide better weather forecasts. Whereas an agency may have two or three weather stations in a particular state, there may be a half dozen or more APRS weather stations in that same state. By collecting the APRS weather station information, the agencies are able to get a fuller picture of the weather conditions in that state.

STILL ANOTHER APRS APPLICATION

Position and weather reporting are the best-known APRS applications, but as Bob Bruninga, WB4APR, "the father of APRS," wrote in the Foreword of this book, these are just the tip of the iceberg. There are other applications that suit APRS just waiting for you to discover and experience. With the assistance of this book, may you begin your journey into the interesting communications world of APRS.

2

HARDWARE

This chapter describes the hardware options that are available for building an APRS station. It also describes how to interconnect the hardware.

WHAT IS APRS?

APRS is an abbreviation for Automatic Position Reporting System. (APRS is sometimes mistaken as being an abbreviation for Automatic Packet Reporting System, but that is incorrect.)
• It is a *system* because it consists of hardware and software components.
• It is a *reporting* system because the system's purpose is to disseminate information about an entity.
• It is a *position* reporting system because the information the system disseminates is related to the location of an entity or some thing.
• It is an *automatic* position reporting system because the location information the system disseminates is done so without human intervention.

WHAT IS THE "SYSTEM" IN APRS?

The basic system consists of an Amateur Radio station (radio, antenna, etc.), a packet radio terminal node controller (TNC), computer, APRS software and the cables to connect the system components together. If the system will be in motion, then add a GPS (Global Positioning System) receiver to the system.

WHAT IS THE "SYSTEM" OF A HOME BASE APRS STATION?

In a typical home base APRS station, the APRS software running on the computer connected to the TNC is programmed with the station's position. The software sends the programmed position information to the TNC when required and the TNC relays the information to the radio for transmission. (Other APRS stations that receive the position packets display the location of the received station on their APRS maps.)

A home base APRS station does not require a GPS receiver because it does not change position. (When initially configuring the APRS software of a home base APRS station, a GPS receiver may be used to determine the station's location, but on a day-to-day basis, a GPS receiver is not required at home.)

WHAT IS THE "SYSTEM" OF A MOBILE APRS STATION?

In a typical mobile APRS station, a Global Positioning System (GPS) receiver calculates the station position from signals received from GPS satellites, then sends the position to the TNC once per second.

Alternatively, a computer can be used instead of a GPS receiver to provide position information for a mobile APRS station, but that requires an operator to manually enter each new position as the mobile station moves. For safety sake, the operator of the mobile vehicle and the operator of the mobile APRS station should not be one in the same.

A mobile APRS station using a GPS receiver to provide position information may also use a computer running APRS software. In this case, the APRS software does not originate the position information. Instead, it relays the position information from the GPS to the TNC when required and it displays its position and the position of other received APRS stations on its APRS maps.

WHAT ARE THE "SYSTEM" REQUIREMENTS FOR THE RADIO EQUIPMENT IN AN APRS STATION?

APRS does not require any special radio equipment. If your

Amateur Radio station performs well with other packet-radio applications, then it should perform well with APRS.

Of course, the radio equipment must be capable of transmitting and receiving signals on the bands you intend to operate.

WHAT ARE THE "SYSTEM" REQUIREMENTS FOR A TNC IN AN APRS STATION?

If you plan to use a computer in your APRS station, then any TNC that is compatible with the original TAPR TNC-2 design is also compatible with APRS. Virtually every TNC sold since 1985 falls into this category, so you should not have any problem finding a suitable TNC for APRS operation with a computer.

However, if you plan to do APRS without a computer, i.e., with a GPS receiver connected to a TNC, then the TNC must be GPS compatible. The March 1994 release of TAPR TNC-2 firmware added support for GPS operation, so if your TNC is compatible with that firmware release, then you may run APRS without a computer.

Beyond GPS compatibility, there are TNCs that offer more with regards to APRS support especially if your APRS station will be a "wide" digipeater, that is, a digipeater providing coverage for a wide geographic area on a full time basis. Recent models of Kantronics and PacComm TNC firmware provide this added APRS support. In addition, the PacComm firmware may be installed in TAPR TNC-2 compatible TNCs like the MFJ-1270 series.

UIDIGI is another alternative firmware for TAPR TNC-2 compatible TNCs. UIDIGI was written from the ground up for APRS digipeater operation and is probably the best firmware for that application. However, UIDIGI is not suitable for non-digipeater APRS stations.

HOW CAN I BE SURE THAT MY TNC IS GPS COMPATIBLE?

If the manual that accompanies your TNC is not clear on the matter, the simplest way to check for GPS-compatibility is to invoke the TNC DISPLAY command. Check the results of the DISPLAY command for any commands whose name is prefixed "NMEA" or "GPS," for example, commands like NMEABCN or GPSTEXT. Then, you know you have a GPS-compatible TNC.

If your TNC is not GPS compatible, you may be able to upgrade its firmware to attain GPS compatibility. However, this is not as easy as it may seem. I recently received e-mail from a frustrated TNC owner who wanted to know if the $20 investment in a firmware upgrade for his XYZ brand TNC would get him GPS compatibility (the manufacturer of the XYZ brand TNC was unable to answer the question).

I told him to ask XYZ if their firmware upgrade is compatible with the March 12, 1994 release of TAPR TNC-2 firmware. If it is, it includes GPS support. If not, then there is no GPS support.

The March 12, 1994 release of TAPR TNC-2 firmware permits the TNC-2 to broadcast one or two National Marine Electronics Association (NMEA) version 2.00 formatted sentences via the Unproto address of a TNC. This enables you to use navigational equipment that output data in NMEA format (like GPS) with a packet radio application such as APRS. (The mating of GPS and APRS facilitates the accurate positioning of APRS objects on APRS maps.)

WHAT ADDED APRS SUPPORT CAN I FIND IN THE FIRMWARE OF CERTAIN TNCS?

In some models of Kantronics and PacComm TNCs, the firmware allows your station to use more than one alias as well as new protocols that provide more efficiency with regards to digipeater. In a similar vein, UIDIGI firmware is optimized for APRS digipeater applications. If you are planning to put a wide digipeater on the air, you should seriously consider the firmware upgrade, especially if other wide digipeaters in your area are using the features provided by the firmware.

WHAT ARE THE "SYSTEM" REQUIREMENTS FOR A COMPUTER IN AN APRS STATION?

The requirements of the computer you intend to use for APRS vary depending upon the version of APRS software you intend to use. In general, microprocessor speed is not a concern, however, RAM and disk storage space may be a concern.

Some versions of APRS have minimum RAM requirements that you must adhere to in order to run the software successfully. Similarly, all versions of APRS have minimum requirements for hard disk space they require for their installation on your computer. More critical may be the amount of disk storage required by the maps you collect for use with the APRS software. The more maps you collect, the more disk space you will eat up. To avoid this, you can store less frequently used maps off line and only load them on your APRS computer when you intend to use them.

WHAT ARE THE "SYSTEM" REQUIREMENTS FOR A GPS RECEIVER IN AN APRS STATION?

The APRS requirement for a GPS receiver is simple. The GPS receiver must output data in the format specified by National Marine Electronics Association (NMEA) standard NMEA-0183. In fact, any navigational equipment (such as LORAN) that outputs data in NMEA-0183 format will also work with APRS. Note that aeronautical GPS equipment does not output NMEA-0183 formatted data.

Once you meet the NMEA-0183 data format requirement, it is your choice as to what kind of GPS receiver to purchase. For mobile and portable APRS applications, the size, weight, and power requirements of the GPS receiver should be a consideration. The smaller, the better should be your goal.

Some GPS receivers have built-in displays that indicate your position. These displays may be used as a substitute for a computer display of APRS maps. For example, the Garmin II PLUS and III GPS receivers not only display your position, but also display the positions of other APRS stations that you receive (if your TNC is configured to send that information to the GPS receiver). In such a configuration, you are able to determine how your position relates to the location of other

APRS stations in your area. In addition, the Garmin III allows you to load road maps from an optional CD-ROM. These maps are displayed along with the position information to provide a display that is competitive with APRS maps displayed by a computer.

Another consideration for mobile and portable applications is the antenna options of the GPS receiver. With APRS GPS applications, you now have to be concerned about two antennas, one for your radio equipment and one for the GPS receiver. Again, the smaller, the better should be your goal. A GPS receiver with a self-contained antenna is your best choice.

WHERE CAN I LEARN MORE ABOUT GPS?

There is a great Web site dedicated to disseminating information about GPS. Two of the fellows who run the site are hams, so it is definitely Amateur Radio and APRS bent. It is Joe Mehaffey, Jack Yeazel, and Dale DePriest's GPS Information Web site (**gpsinformation.net/**) Joe is W2JO; Jack is N4TEB.

The home page of the Web site contains a long list of links to educational articles written by the guys or information written by others and located on other Web sites. The guys grouped the links into various categories in order to facilitate finding the information you need more quickly.

The page has links describing how GPS works, hardware FAQs (frequently-asked questions), hardware and software reviews, geographical information related to GPS (maps, datum, waypoint lists, formulas, etc.), GPS accessories (e.g., parts for building your own Garmin GPS cables), tips and how-tos (like how to build your own GPS antenna). Sprinkled throughout the list of links are ham radio and APRS references. And if you cannot find it here, you might find it under Other GPS Information Sites links.

HOW DO I INTERCONNECT THE TNC AND RADIO IN AN APRS STATION?

The radio side of the TNC is the simpler connection. The TNC radio port, which is typically a female DB-9 or 5-pin DIN connector, provides connections for audio output, audio input, press-to-talk (PTT), and ground.

Connect the audio output of the TNC to the audio input of your transmitter/transceiver. Typically, the audio input of your radio equipment is the microphone input (MIC) connection, but some transceivers have separate audio inputs for AFSK tones (sometimes labeled "AFSK in"). If such a connection is available, it is better to use that connection rather than the microphone input because you will not have to disconnect the TNC from the microphone connector whenever you want to use the radio in the voice mode. In addition, the AFSK input may bypass circuits in the transceiver that are intended for voice and/ or may insert circuits intended for data. Voice circuits are not necessarily beneficial to data transmission, so bypassing them is a good thing. On the other hand, circuits intended to improve data transmission should be used whenever possible.

Connect the audio input of the TNC to the audio output of your receiver/transceiver. Typically, the audio output of your radio is a speaker or headphone connector, but some radios have optional audio outputs (sometimes labeled "AFSK out"). Again, connection to such an optional audio output avoids TNC disconnection when you switch to voice and may bypass circuits intended for processing voice and/or insert circuits intended for processing data. If your radio does not have separate AFSK jacks, the phone patch input and output jacks often provide an acceptable alternative.

Connect the PTT line of the TNC to a PTT connection on your transmitter/transceiver. Usually, PTT is available at the

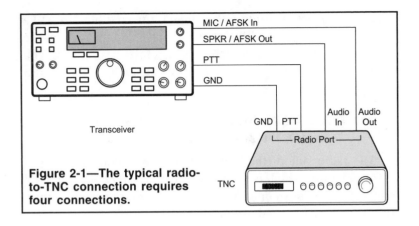

MIC / AFSK In
SPKR / AFSK Out
PTT
GND

Transceiver

GND   PTT   Audio   Audio
               In   Out

Radio Port

Figure 2-1—The typical radio-to-TNC connection requires four connections.

TNC

microphone connector, but the PTT line is sometimes brought out to another connector as well. Again, connection to the optional PTT jack is preferable; this avoids cable changes when you switch modes.

Finally, connect the TNC ground to the ground connection that accompanies the other connections to your transceiver (or transmitter and receiver), that is, the ground that accompanies the radio's MIC, PTT, speaker, or AFSK In/Out connections. (**Figure 2-1** illustrates the typical TNC-to-radio connection.)

The only complication in making connections on the radio side of the TNC is when the radio is a VHF or UHF handheld transceiver that uses a common conductor for audio input (MIC) and PTT. Simply connecting the TNC audio output and PTT leads to the common connection on the radio will not work.

To make the connection successfully, a resistor and a capacitor, are required as illustrated in **Figure 2-2**. Resistor and capacitor values of 1 to 2 kΩ and .01 to 1.0 µF are typical, but these values depend on the radio used, so consult the manual that accompanies your radio for the values that are required.

HOW DO I INTERCONNECT THE TNC AND COMPUTER IN AN APRS STATION?

The serial ports of most TNCs are compatible with Electronic Industries Association (EIA) interface standard EIA-

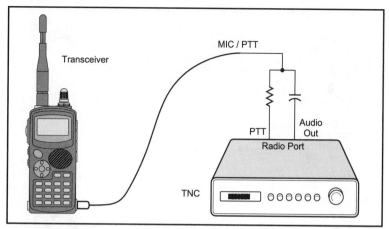

Figure 2-2—When the radio uses a common MIC/PTT conductor, the radio-to-TNC connection requires a resistor and capacitor to isolate the signals at the TNC.

232. This standard defines 25 signals that may be transferred via the interface, however, the TNC only needs three of those signals to communicate with a computer and GPS receiver: Transmitted Data, Received Data, and Signal Ground.

In most cases, the TNC uses a female 25-pin D-type (DB-25) connector for the serial port. This necessitates using a male DB-25 connector with pins 2, 3 and 7 cabled to a connector that mates with the serial port of the computer.

The computer typically has a male DB-25 or male 9-pin D-type (DB-9) connector for its serial port. This necessitates using a female DB-25 or DB-9 connector at the computer end of the computer-to-TNC connection. For DB-25-to-DB-25 cabling, pins 2, 3 and 7 (Transmitted Data, Received Data, and Signal Ground) are connected between each DB-25 connector, as illustrated in **Figure 2-3A**.

For DB-25-to-DB-9 cabling, pins 2 and 3 (Transmitted Data and Received Data) are connected between each connector and pin 7 (Signal Ground) of the DB-25 is connected to pin 5 of the DB-9, as illustrated in **Figure 2-3B**.

To avoid the time and expense of building a cable for the

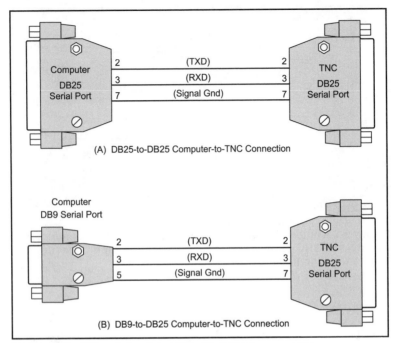

Figure 2-3—The minimal cabling for TNC-to-computer connections requires three wires.

computer-to-TNC connection, you can use the cable connecting your computer serial port to your external telephone line modem, if you have one.

Since the TNC serial port is EIA-232 compatible, it is compatible with the serial ports of most computers with the notable exception of computers that use a Universal Serial Bus (USB) connector instead of an EIA interface connector. To work around this situation, USB adapters are available to permit you to connect an EIA-232 serial port device (like a TNC) to a computer that uses a USB connector.

HOW DO I CONNECT THE GPS RECEIVER IN AN APRS STATION?

For a GPS-to-TNC or GPS-to-computer connection, you use the same connector and cabling at the TNC or computer end that you use for the TNC-to-computer connection (typically, a male DB-25 or female DB-9 with wire connections at pins 2, 3, and 7). However, there is no typical connector for the GPS end of this connection. Different GPS receivers use different types of connectors. Therefore, you must obtain the appropriate connector for the GPS receiver you intend to use and wire it correctly to the TNC or computer connector. Hopefully, the documentation accompanying your GPS receiver provides the pin-out for the connector.

HOW DO I INTERCONNECT THE TNC, COMPUTER AND GPS RECEIVER IN AN APRS STATION?

The TNC-to-computer connection described above is fine if you do not intend to use a GPS receiver in your APRS application, for example, in a home base installation. And the

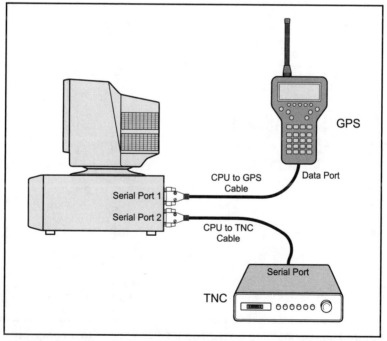

Figure 2-4—Connecting a TNC and a GPS receiver to a computer is straightforward when the computer has two serial ports.

GPS-to-TNC connection is suitable if you do not intend to use a computer in your APRS application, for example, in a tracker installation. However, if you intend to use both a computer and a GPS receiver, then you must make different connections.

If your computer has two serial ports or USB connectors available, then use the TNC-to-computer cabling, described above, to connect your TNC to one port. Use the TNC-to-GPS receiver cabling, described above, to connect your GPS receiver to the other port, then configure your APRS software so that it is aware of these connections, which are illustrated in **Figure 2-4**.

If your computer has only one serial port or USB connector available, then you can use a hardware single port switch (HSP) cable, which is available from a number of sources (Kantronics, MFJ, PacComm). Simply, connect the HSP cable to the serial port or USB connector (via a USB adapter) of your computer, then use the cabling described earlier to connect your TNC and

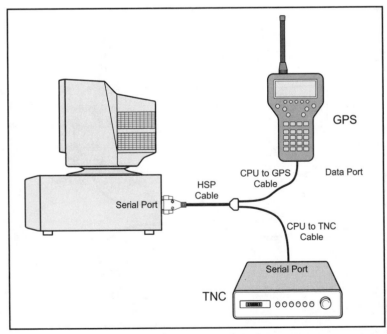

Figure 2-5—Connecting a TNC and a GPS receiver to a computer requires a hardware single port switch (HSP) cable when the computer has only one serial port.

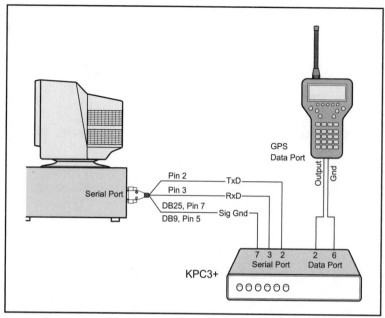

Figure 2-6—If your TNC is a Kantronics KPC-3 Plus with firmware version 8.3 (or later), you can connect your computer to its serial port and the GPS receiver to its radio port.

GPS receiver to the HSP cable, as illustrated in **Figure 2-5**.

If your computer has only one serial port or USB connector, an alternative to the HSP cable is available if your TNC is a Kantronics KPC-3 Plus with firmware version 8.3 or later or a PacComm PicoPacket TNC with dual serial ports. In either case, you connect the GPS to the TNC instead of your computer.

If your TNC is a Kantronics KPC-3 Plus with firmware version 8.3 or later, you connect your computer to the TNC as described above, i.e., connect the computer to the male DB-25 connector at the TNC end via its pins 2, 3, and 7 or 5 (Transmitted Data, Received Data, and Signal Ground). Instead of connecting the GPS receiver to the KPC-3 Plus serial port, you connect it to the TNC radio port with the GPS output connected to pin 2 and GPS ground to pin 6, as illustrated in **Figure 2-6**. The radio connections to the radio port remain the same.

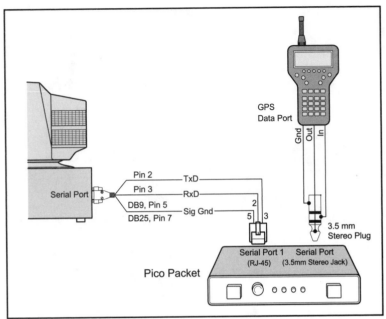

Figure 2-7—If your TNC is a PacComm PicoPacket with dual serial ports, you can connect your computer to one serial port and the GPS receiver to the other serial port.

When you program the TNC, you must enable this GPS connection via the GPSPORT command (for example, GPSPORT 4800 NORMAL CHECKSUM). You must also disable external carrier detect via the CD command (CD INTERNAL or CD SOFTWARE).

If your TNC is a PacComm PicoPacket with the dual serial port option, you connect your computer to one serial port via an RJ-45 plug and your GPS receiver to the other serial port via a 3.5 mm stereo plug. (The PicoPacket uses RJ-45 connectors for its first serial port and its radio port.) These connections are illustrated in **Figure 2-7**.

Another alternative is to use a PacComm PicoPacket TNC with the internal GPS receiver option. In this case, you only have to connect the TNC to your radio and computer.

HOW DO I CONNECT KENWOOD TH-D7A TRANSCEIVER FOR APRS OPERATION?

There are two ways you can use the Kenwood TH-D7 transceiver for APRS: as a standalone APRS station by means of its built-in APRS software or as the radio and TNC portion of an APRS station by configuring its built-in TNC using any version of APRS.

As a standalone APRS station, you have to make a connection to the radio only if you are using a GPS receiver. In that case, you use the cable with the 2.5 mm 3-conductor plug that was included with the TH-D7. Connect the red wire in the cable to the GPS data output, connect the white wire to the GPS data input and connect the shield to GPS ground. Then, connect the 3-conductor plug to the GPS port of the TH-D7. **Figure 2-8** illustrates this connection.

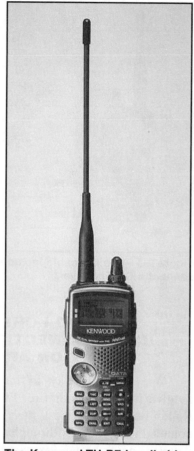

The Kenwood TH-D7 handheld transceiver.

To use the TH-D7 with a version of APRS running on a computer, connect the radio to the computer with the optional Kenwood PG-4W cable. Connect the 3-conductor plug of the PG-4W to the PC port of the radio and connect the DB-9 connector to the serial port of your computer. If the serial port of your computer is not a DB-9 or is a USB connector, you must acquire an adapter (for example, a DB-9-to-DB-25 adapter for DB-25 serial ports) to complete the connection.

If you plan to use a GPS receiver in this configuration, connect the GPS receiver to the TH-D7 as described above and illustrated in Figure 2-8.

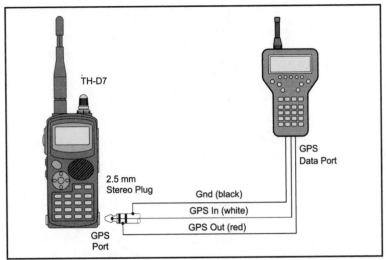

Figure 2-8—Use the cable included with the Kenwood TH-D7 to connect a GPS receiver.

HOW DO I CHECK THAT THE INTERCONNECTIONS OF AN APRS STATION ARE WORKING?

One of the best ways to find out if your installation works is to give it a test under fire. FCC regulations permit Amateur Radio operators to test their equipment on the air, so try connecting to yourself through a local station and send some test data (the quick brown fox works just as well on packet radio as it does on RTTY).

Since you may have not installed and configured the APRS software yet, you will need a simple terminal program to perform the test. *HyperTerminal*, which is an Accessories program included in *Windows 95/98/2000/NT/XP*, is adequate for this purpose. For other computer platforms, you can use a public domain terminal program that is suitable.

After you have the terminal software up and running, try connecting to yourself. To do so, the other station you are connecting through must have its digipeater function enable (DIGI ON). If it is disabled, you can still obtain some test results because if your installation is working, you will at least be able

Sound Card as "TNC"

With proliferation of sound cards in computers, it was inevitable that hams would begin writing software that uses the sound cards as digital communication modems. George Rossopoulos, SV2AGW, wrote a free *Windows* program called *AGWPE* (AGW Packet Engine) that allows a PC to function as packet TNC. *AGWPE* is directly compatible with a number of APRS programs such as *UI-View*.

The only external connections are the audio cables to and from your radio, and a connection to the PC serial port to allow the computer to switch the radio from receive to transmit. These connections are typically achieved using sound card interfaces such as those manufactured by MFJ (**www.mfjenterprises.com**), West Mountain Radio (**www.westmountainradio.com**) or TigerTronics (**www.tigertronics.com**). These are the same interfaces that hams use to operate other digital modes such as PSK31.

Ralph Milnes, KC2RLM, has an excellent *AGWPE* tutorial on the Web at **www.qsl.net/soundcardpacket/**. The *AGWPE* software is available for download at **www.raag.org/sv2agw/inst.htm**.

to connect and disconnect from that station.

To connect to yourself, at the TNC command prompt, type:

C URCALL V THRCALL <Enter>

...where URCALL is your call sign and SSID (if any) and THRCALL is the call sign and SSID (if any) of the station through which you are trying to digipeat.

If you are able to connect with yourself and successfully receive the test data, your installation is working.

If you are unable to connect with yourself (or worse), read further for the possible solution to the problem.

HOW DO I TROUBLESHOOT PROBLEMS IN THE INTERCONNECTIONS OF AN APRS STATION?

You don't have to be a rocket scientist to figure out why your installation is not working. All you need is a little help from your friendly troubleshooting guide, which is presented in **Table 2-1**.

If your TNC is functioning properly, that is, it was not dead on arrival or is not on the verge of death, then this troubleshooting guide will be able to diagnose the majority of problems

Table 2-1
TNC Troubleshooting Guide

Trouble	Possible Causes
Nothing happens after turning on the TNC power switch	Power source problem; check connection between TNC and power supply; check that the connection is tight; check connection wiring; check that an external switch (such as a wall switch) that controls the power supply is not turned off.
No sign-on message after power-up; front panel indicators are lit	Connection between TNC and computer serial port; check that the connection is tight; check the Received Data (pin 3) and Signal Ground (DB-25 pin 7/DB-9 pin 5) leads.
Sign-on message is garbled.	Incompatibility between TNC and computer serial port; check that the serial port data rate, parity and character bit length of the TNC and computer serial port are equal.
TNC does not respond to keyboard input.	Connection between TNC and computer serial port; check that connection is tight; check the Transmitted Data (pin 2) and Signal Ground (DB-25 pin 7/DB-9 pin 5) leads.
Cannot copy packets. DCD Front-panel indicator does not light when signal is heard	Connection between TNC and radio; check that the connection is tight; check the connection between the TNC audio input and radio audio output. Receiver audio is set too low; turn up the volume.

that you are likely to encounter with your installation.

If your packet radio controller is a multiport and/or multimode controller, that adds complexity to troubleshooting your installation, complexity that is not covered by the guide. If the troubleshooting guide is unable to solve the problem in a multiport and/or multimode environment, then check that the problem is not related to selecting the incorrect port or incorrect mode. Your equipment manual may offer some assistance.

By the way, some TNCs provide their own self-contained diagnostics. Check the TNC manual to find out what, if anything, is available and, if all else fails, try them.

Cannot copy packets from other stations; DCD front panel indicator lights when signal is heard.	Connection between TNC and computer serial port; check that the connection is tight; check the Received Data lead, pin 3. Receiver audio is set too high; turn down the volume
Cannot copy packets from other stations; DCD front panel indicator lights when signal is heard. Garbled characters appear on computer display.	Incompatibility between TNC and channel activity; check that the radio port data rate, parity and character bit length of the TNC and other stations on the air are equal.
Transmitter does not key although PTT indicator lights.	Connection between TNC and radio; check that the connection is tight; check the PTT and ground leads.
Transmitter is keyed continuously	Connection between TNC and radio; check that the connection is tight; check the PTT and ground leads.
Other stations cannot copy your packets, but you can copy their packets	Connection between TNC and radio; check that the connection is tight; check the connection between the TNC audio output and radio audio input. TNC audio output is set incorrectly; check deviation. TXdelay is set too low; increase TXdelay by 10 ms increments.

HOW DO I SET THE DEVIATION OF MY APRS STATION TRANSMITTER?

In the FM mode, information is encoded by varying the carrier frequency of the FM signal, while amplitude is encoded by controlling the amount that the carrier frequency is varied or deviated. This change, shift or deviation of the carrier frequency is proportional to the amplitude of the input signal. If the amplitude of the input signal is zero, there will be no change (no deviation) in the carrier frequency and there will be nothing heard in the receiver at the other end. As the amplitude of the input signal increases, the amount by which the carrier shifts (or deviates) increases, too.

For this explanation, let us assume that each volt of amplitude corresponds to 1 kHz of deviation. Therefore, if you modulate a 1500 Hz tone at a carrier frequency of 147.000 MHz with 2 volts of amplitude, the carrier will deviate 2 kHz, that is, between 146.999 and 147.001 MHz. If you modulate the same tone at the same carrier frequency with 4 volts of amplitude, the carrier will deviate 4 kHz (between 146.998 and 147.002 MHz).

Ideally, the deviation of your signal should fall between 3.0 and 3.5 kHz. It will be hard to decode your packets if your signal is below 3.0 kHz of deviation. The TNC at the other end cannot decode your packets if it can't hear them! On the other hand, it will be difficult to decode your packets if your deviation is too much above 3.5 kHz. Your transmitter cannot deviate signals much higher than that. Too high a deviation causes your signal to be clipped by the audio stages of your transmitter and results in a distorted signal in the receiver at the other end of the connection, that is, a signal that a TNC will have a tough time decoding.

To achieve the best throughput of your packets, you must set your FM signal deviation within the ideal range. To do this, you need a deviation meter and an alignment tool that allows you to adjust the audio output level control of your TNC. (Some TNCs, like the Kantronics KPC-3 Plus, allow you to adjust the level in software.)

To check the deviation of your transmitter, connect it to a dummy load and start transmitting a dead carrier, that is, without

The PacComm PicoPacket TNC shown with internal circuit boards.

audio input, while you attempt to tune in your signal with the deviation meter. If the meter has a speaker output, I recommend attaching a speaker to it to simplify the tuning procedure. With a speaker attached, you simply tune the meter until you hear the squelch break, then you continue tuning very slowly until you tune to the center of the signal.

Next, you put your TNC in the calibration mode by typing at the command prompt:

CAL ON <ENTER>

In the calibration mode, check the deviation as you transmit, in succession, the high and low frequency tones of the TNC (pressing your keyboard Space Bar switches between the high and low tones). If the deviation of a tone is too high or too low, adjust the level accordingly using the TNC audio output control. The location and accessibility of the audio output control varies with each TNC. Check your TNC manual for its location.

If your TNC does not have such a control, you will have to adjust the microphone gain of your transmitter. If that is the case, check the radio manual for the location and accessibility of that control. After you adjust the audio output control, check both tones again to make sure they are still adjusted correctly.

Lacking a deviation meter, you can get your deviation in the ballpark by using your ear. Using a separate receiver, monitor the local APRS channel and compare your APRS station's transmitted audio to the audio of the other APRS stations in your area. If your station's audio is noticeably higher or lower than the other station's in your area, then adjust your station's audio level to match the audio level of the other stations.

3

SOFTWARE VERSIONS

This chapter describes the various versions of APRS software that are currently available.

WHAT APRS SOFTWARE IS AVAILABLE FOR MY COMPUTER?

There are a variety of APRS applications available for a variety of computers or more specifically, computer operating systems (OS).

- For the *Linux* OS, there are *X-APRS* and *XASTIR*.
- For the Mac OS, there are *MacAPRS* and *XASTIR*. (*XASTIR* runs under *X-Windows* that is included in the Mac OS.)
- For the *MS-DOS* OS, there is *APRS*, the first APRS application. To avoid confusion, I will refer to this version of *APRS* as *APRSdos* throughout this book.
- For the Palm OS, there is *pocketAPRS*.
- For the Unix OS, there is *XASTIR*.
- For the *Windows* (16-bit) OS, there are *UI-View* and *WinAPRS*.
- For the *Windows* (32-bit) OS, there are *APRS+SA*, *APRSPoint*, *UI-View* and *WinAPRS*.
- For the *Windows CE* OS, there is *APRS/CE*.

APRS/CE is a *Windows CE* OS version of APRS written by Rob Wittner, KZ5RW, that runs on *Windows CE*-compatible hand-held personal digital assistants (PDA).

APRS+SA is a *Windows* (32-bit) OS version of APRS written by Brent Hildebrand, KH2Z, that uses Delorme *Street Atlas USA* software (**www.delorme.com/**) for its maps.

APRSdos is a *DOS* version of APRS written by Bob

Bruninga, WB4APR. Its minimum computer requirements are a PC running *DOS* with an 8088 microprocessor (or better), a standard CGA, EGA or VGA monitor, and 550 Kbytes of free RAM. *APRSdos* does not work with non-standard video cards, such as the Hercules video card.

APRSPoint is a *Windows* (32-bit) OS version of *APRS* written by Michael Cai, KF6ZDM, that uses Microsoft's *MapPoint* (**mappoint.msn.com/(fu3dn555ekhpnh454u42ho3d)/Home.aspx**) for its maps.

MacAPRS is a Mac OS version of *APRS* written by Keith Sproul, WU2Z, and Mark Sproul, KB2ICI. The minimum computer requirements of *MacAPRS* are a Macintosh computer running System 7.0 or later. The recommended computer configuration is a color Macintosh with 8 Mbytes of RAM.

pocketAPRS is a version of *APRS* written by Mike Musick, NØQBF, that runs on a 3Com Palm III Connected Organizer, which is a hand-held personal digital assistant (PDA).

UI-View is a *Windows* (16- or 32-bit) version of *APRS* written by Roger Barker, G4IDE. Besides working with TNCs in the terminal mode, it also supports TNCs in KISS mode, AGWPE host mode and BPQ host mode. The 32-bit version also supports WA8DED/TF host mode, and the variant of it used in the SCS PTC-II and PTC-IIe multimode controllers. Host mode support means that *UI-View* can be used with an extremely wide range of packet hardware and allows up to 16 RF ports to be used.

WinAPRS is a *Windows* (16- or 32-bit) version of APRS written by Keith

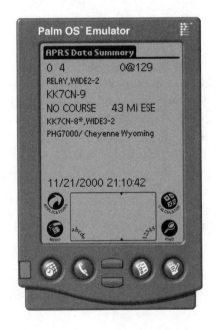

pocketAPRS in action.

Sproul, WU2Z, and Mark Sproul, KB2ICI. The minimum computer requirements of *WinAPRS* are a PC with a 386 microprocessor running *Windows 95*. The recommended computer configuration is a PC with a 486 microprocessor and a 33-MHz clock with 8 Mbytes of RAM running *Windows 95*, *Windows NT* or *Windows 3.1*. Running under *Windows 3.1* requires the installation of the Win32S library, which is available at **www.ncsa.uiuc.edu/SDG/Software/mosaic-w/faq/win32.html**.

 X-APRS is a *Linux* version of APRS written by Keith Sproul, WU2Z, and Mark Sproul, KB2ICI.

 XASTIR is a *Linux*/UNIX version of *APRS* written by Frank Giannandrea, KCØDGE, and The *XASTIR* Group that supports over 21 operating systems and 117 map formats.

WHERE CAN I GET APRS SOFTWARE?

 The primary source for APRS software is the Internet. You may download each APRS application using the URL following its name. You may obtain most versions of APRS from TAPR's Web site (its URL is **ftp://ftp.tapr.org/software_lib/aprssig**).

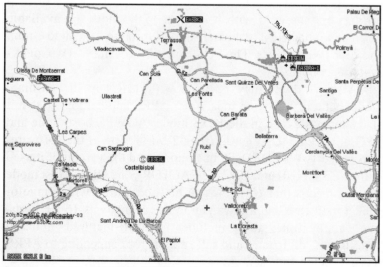

An image from *XASTIR*, APRS software for *Linux*.

- *APRS/CE*: **www.tapr.org/~aprsce/**
- *APRS+SA*: **www.tapr.org/~kh2z/aprsplus/**
- *APRSdos*: **web.usna.navy.mil/~bruninga/aprs.html**
- *APRSPoint*: **www.aprspoint.com/**
- *MacAPRS*: **aprs.rutgers.edu/**
- *pocketAPRS*: **www.pocketAPRS.com/**
- *UI-View*: **www.peak-systems.com/**
- *WinAPRS*: **aprs.rutgers.edu/**
- *X-APRS*: **aprs.rutgers.edu/**
- *XASTIR*: **www.XASTIR.org/**

WHAT IS THE MOST POPULAR APRS APPLICATION?

These days, *Windows*-based *UI-View* is likely the most popular APRS application. Roger Barker, G4IDE, is the man responsible for this version of APRS software, which swept Europe and is now sweeping the rest of the APRS world.

Roger's software has a lot going for it. A variety of map formats may be used with it, add-on applications are available for it, and it has great technical support through its Yahoo Group and its Web site, The *UI-View* Web site (**www.peak-systems.com/**).

Also, *UI-View* may be used with TNCs in the terminal mode, but it differs from most other APRS applications in that it also supports TNCs in the KISS mode, AGWPE host mode and BPQ host mode. *UI-View32* (the 32-bit version of the software) also supports WA8DED/TF host mode, and the variant of it used in the SCS PTC-II and PTC-IIe PACTOR controllers. Host mode support means that *UI-View* can be used with a wide range of packet hardware and allows you to use as many as 16 RF ports. The application also includes a full-featured internal "intelligent" digipeater and full support for connecting to APRS servers on the Internet.

The *UI-View* Web Site provides everything you need to

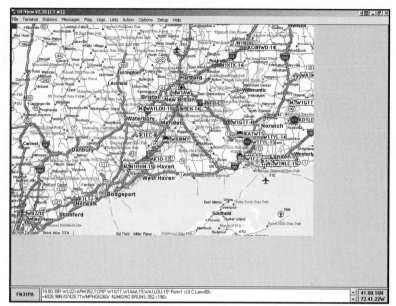

UI-View, the most popular APRS software for *Windows*.

know to get started, including links for downloading the software, maps, add-ons, plug-ins and technical support. There are also links to other Web sites where you can obtain more maps, more tools and more!

4
SOFTWARE INSTALLATION

In my previous APRS books, I described in detail how to install and configure each version of APRS software. Since the number of APRS applications has quadrupled since the previous book was published, describing how to install and configure each version of software would result in a book of encyclopedic proportions. As an alternative, this chapter describes how to install and configure APRS software "generically." Most of the configuration parameters are common in each version of APRS software, so this generic description will describe in detail the parameters that the user needs to get APRS up and running.

HOW DO I CONFIGURE APRS SOFTWARE?

The first time you run APRS software, there are some minimum parameters that you must set in order to operate APRS properly.

Call Sign and SSID—You must configure the APRS software with an Amateur Radio call sign and optionally, an SSID if one is desired. An SSID (for secondary station identifier) is a number (0-15) that follows a packet radio station call sign (and a hyphen). It is used to differentiate between two or more packet radio stations operating under the same call sign. For example, my APRS digipeater is WA1LOU-15 and my APRS mobile station is WA1LOU-8. If you do not specify an SSID number, zero is used by default.

Alias—This parameter indicates the alias for your APRS station (RELAY or WIDE).

Symbol—You must select a symbol to represent your station on the APRS maps. Refer to **Table 4-1** for the list of selectable symbols.

Position Text—This is a short string of text that the APRS application sends whenever it transmits your station's position packet. The posit text can be related to your name, location, or whatever you feel is appropriate. There is a timer setting that determines how often you want APRS to transmit a position packet. Stationary stations should set this timer to transmit once every 30 minutes or so, while mobile stations should set this timer to transmit every 1 or 2 minutes.

Status Text—This is a short string of text that the APRS application sends whenever it transmits your station's beacon. The status text can be related to your name, location, or whatever you feel is appropriate. There is a timer setting that determines how often you want APRS to transmit a beacon.

Port—This parameter indicates which computer port(s) is used to connect your TNC and other equipment (GPS receiver, weather station, etc) used in your APRS station.

Baud Rate—This parameter indicates the baud rate used for communications between your TNC and computer. You must also set the baud rate for any other APRS equipment (GPS receiver, weather station, etc) connected to your APRS computer.

Data Bits—This parameter indicates the number of bits that represent an alphanumeric or control character used in communications between your TNC and computer. The choices may be 5, 6, 7 or 8. You must also set the number of data bits for any other APRS equipment (GPS receiver, weather station, etc) connected to your APRS computer.

Stop Bits—This parameter indicates the number of bits that follow a character (to indicate its end) used in communications between your TNC and computer. The choices may be 1, 1.5 or 2. You must also set the number of stop bits for any other APRS equipment (GPS receiver, weather station, etc) connected to your APRS computer.

Handshaking Protocol—This parameter indicates the protocol used for coordinating communications between your TNC and computer. The choices may be None, XON/XOFF, DTR & CTS, DTR only, and CTS only. When in doubt, select None. You must also set the handshaking protocol used for any other APRS equipment (GPS receiver, weather station, etc) connected to your APRS computer.

TNC—The APRS software needs to know what brand and/or model of TNC is connected to the APRS computer and whether that TNC is dual-band or single-band TNC.

RF Equipment—The transmitter power, antenna height, and antenna gain (power, height, and gain or PHG) are parameters that the APRS software uses to determine the radio coverage of your APRS station, which can be displayed on the maps of most APRS applications.

You enter your transmitter power in watts. Typically, the maximum entry in this field is 81 W. Entering anything larger than 81 results in 81. The purpose of this limitation is to promote the use of minimum power in APRS networks.

The antenna height parameter is antenna height above average terrain (HAAT), not antenna height above sea level. This parameter is discussed in detail below.

You enter the antenna gain in dB. Some APRS applications also have an antenna direction parameter, i.e., the direction (in degrees) that station antenna favors if the antenna is a directional antenna or for conditions where local terrain effects the operation of an omnidirectional antenna.

UTC Offset—This parameter indicates the number of hours (+ or −) your local time differs from Greenwich Mean/Universal Time.

Validation or Registration Number—If you have registered your APRS software, enter the registration or validation number in the software to avoid reconfiguring the software each time you start APRS.

Heading and Speed—If your station is mobile and without a GPS receiver, use the Heading parameter to enter your station's compass direction in degrees and the Speed parameter to enter your station's miles-per-hour.

Station coordinates (latitude and longitude), height above average terrain (HAAT), and digipeater (Unproto) path are critical parameters that I discuss in detail in the following questions.

HOW DO I DETERMINE
MY STATIONS COORDINATES?

For a home or base APRS station, you need to determine your

exact location and configure APRS with that information in order for APRS to operate as accurately as possible.

A city, town or street address is not accurate enough. Rather, you need your station coordinates, that is, the latitude and longitude of your APRS station, preferably in degrees, minutes, and seconds. There are a few ways to obtain this information.

An easy, accurate but expensive way to obtain your station coordinates is by using a GPS receiver that provides that information. If you know someone who has a GPS receiver and is willing to help you out, then you have a substantial economic savings without forgoing the ease and accuracy of determining your coordinates. If you purchased a GPS receiver to use with APRS, then you have it made. However, I would not advise purchasing a GPS receiver just to obtain your station coordinates for the sake of APRS accuracy. There are less expensive and still accurate ways of determining your coordinates.

You can look it up. Using a good map of your area, you can determine your coordinates with fairly good accuracy. Topographic maps like the 7.5-minute quadrangles published by the United States Geological Survey (USGS, Washington, DC 20242) are perfect for determining your coordinates. The USGS maps are inexpensive and very detailed. If you don't live in an urban area, the building that houses your APRS station likely appears on the USGS quadrangle for your area. So, that should permit you to accurately determine your coordinates.

You can also look up your coordinates in an atlas. The maps in an atlas are not as detailed as the USGS quadrangles, so determining your coordinates using a map in an atlas produces less accurate results, however, you can use those results as a starting point and fine tune them later.

Some atlases list the major cities and towns in the world and sometimes the latitude and longitude of each city and town is also listed. Some almanacs provide similar lists, but only for the major cities. The accuracy of such lists varies depending upon how close you live to the location in your town or city where the coordinates were determined. If you live over the town hall or post office, you are in pretty good shape using the coordinates from an atlas or almanac, however, if you live on the back forty of Old Macdonald's farm, the coordinates may be bit off.

If you are on the Internet, you can obtain your coordinates from the Geographic Nameserver Web site run by the Massachusetts Institute of Technology (MIT). To look up your coordinates, go to the Web site (**www.mit.edu:8001/geo**), type your location in the Placename: field, and click on the **Submit** button. In a few seconds, the Web site provides you with information concerning your location including its latitude and longitude in degrees, minutes and seconds. For example, when I entered Wolcott, CT, the Web site responded with the following:

Placename: Wolcott
State: Connecticut
County: New Haven County
Lat/Long: 41:36:08 N 072:59:14 W

This name server is not US-centric. It also will find the coordinates for more populous international locations, too, for example, entering Toronto resulted in coordinates for Toronto, Ontario, Canada, as well as, a handful of locales in the US named "Toronto." And entering "Warsaw" resulted in the coordinates for the capitol of Poland, but entering "Krakow" came up with nothing, so your mileage may vary using this server for locations outside the US.

The USGS runs a Web site that is strictly US-centric (**geonames.usgs.gov/pls/gnis/web_query.gnis_web_query_ form**). There you can get the coordinates for locations throughout the United States and its territories.

WHAT IS HEIGHT ABOVE AVERAGE TERRAIN (HAAT)?

While configuring APRS, you will be prompted to enter your station's Height Above Average Terrain (HAAT). APRS uses HAAT to calculate and display your station's coverage on the APRS maps.

HAAT is not the same as your height above sea level. HAAT is the height of your antenna as it relates to the average height of the terrain in the 10-mile radius surrounding your station's antenna. For example, if your antenna is 1000 feet above sea level and the average height of the terrain in the 10-mile radius surrounding the antenna is 900 feet, your HAAT is 100 feet.

HOW DO I DETERMINE MY STATION'S HEIGHT ABOVE AVERAGE TERRAIN (HAAT)?

To calculate HAAT, use a topographical map and record the height of the terrain in 2-mile increments along the eight compass directions (N, NE, E, SE, S, SW, W, and NW) radiating 10-miles out from your antenna. For example, in the northeast direction, you would record the height of the terrain at the points that are 2, 4, 6, 8 and 10 miles northeast of your antenna.

When you are finished, you should have 40 points recorded. Add them together and divide the sum by 40. The result of this calculation is the average height of the terrain in the 10-mile radius surrounding your station. Subtract this figure from the height of your antenna above sea level. The difference is your HAAT.

WHAT DIGIPEATER (UNPROTO) PATH SHOULD I USE FOR MY APRS STATION'S TRANSMISSIONS?

The AX.25 Unproto command determines the digipeaters used to propagate the packets transmitted by your APRS station. For example, if Unproto is set to VIA A,B, your packet is initially retransmitted by digipeater A. Then, it is retransmitted by digipeater B (assuming that digipeater B hears digipeater A's retransmission of your packet). In this example, your "digipeater path" is VIA A,B or simply, A,B.

The digipeater path that your APRS station uses is critical to its ability to be received by other APRS stations. If your path is set incorrectly, then only the stations that can hear you directly will hear you, while the stations beyond the range of your transmissions won't hear you. For example, if your path is A,B, but digipeater A can't hear you, then none of the digipeaters in your path will retransmit your packets.

APRS simplifies the selection of your digipeater path by means of the alias command that is included in the firmware of your TNC. (Alias permits a packet station to use one or more station identifications in addition to the identification, typically, the station call sign that is programmed into the TNC via the MYCall command.)

In theory, all APRS stations may be used to relay the packets of less fortunate APRS stations, i.e., stations running less power, less antenna, and in less favorable locations. So, it is suggested that all APRS stations use an alias of RELAY.

If your digipeater path is RELAY,A,B instead of A,B your chances of getting your packets retransmitted by digipeaters A and B is enhanced. Any APRS RELAY station that hears your initial packet will retransmit it. Assuming that one of those RELAY stations is more fortunate than your station, i.e., more power, more antenna, and more HAAT, then digipeater A is more likely to hear RELAY's retransmission of your packet (and digipeater A will retransmit it, too.)

To further simplify matters, it is suggested that APRS digipeaters use an alias of WIDE (for wide area digipeater). In the RELAY,A,B digipeater path example, if your packet was retransmitted by one or more RELAYs, your packet would go no further if digipeater A could not hear any of the RELAYs. But, what if another digipeater (C, D, or E) heard one of the RELAYs? If C, D or E was a WIDE digipeater and your path was RELAY,WIDE, instead of RELAY,A,B then your packet would be retransmitted by WIDE C, D and/or E.

When you configure your APRS software, you can ignore the digipeater path setting and let the software use its default path. The default settings of your packet paths allow you to get up and running without having an intimate knowledge of your local APRS network. Depending on the version of APRS you are using, the default path is typically either RELAY or WIDE, or a combination of RELAY and WIDE.

On the other hand, you may fine-tune the digipeater path setting to be compatible with local APRS network, especially after you become familiar with your local APRS network. For example, if you know which RELAYs and WIDEs can hear your station, program the RELAY and WIDE call signs into your path rather than using aliases. This promotes network efficiency and throughput. If your path is A,B instead of RELAY,WIDE, instead of hitting two or more RELAYs or WIDEs and causing packet collisions, you will hit only A, then only B, thus, reducing the potential for collision and increasing throughput. This applies to all fixed stations and any mobile stations that travel the same, short distance on a regular basis. Mobile stations passing through an unfamiliar APRS network are a different matter. They should stick with generic paths like RELAY,WIDE.

HOW DO I SET UP A HOME/BASE STATION TO SERVE AS AN APRS DIGIPEATER?

Any fixed APRS station can serve as an APRS digipeater and is encouraged to do so in order to fill in the nooks and crannies of the APRS network. Well-situated, that is, highly elevated, fixed APRS stations are encouraged to serve as wide digipeaters in order to fill in the wide expanses of the APRS network.

The alias of a fixed APRS station that is not a wide digipeater should be set to RELAY and its path should be set to WIDE,WIDE. The alias of a wide digipeater should be set to WIDE and its path should be set to WIDE,WIDE.

Ideally, wide digipeaters should use a current generation TNC that may be configured with multiple aliases. One alias should be set to RELAY and another alias to WIDE. In this way, a wide digipeater can also fill in as a RELAY digipeater for those nooks and crannies not covered by other RELAY digipeaters.

A work-around for TNCs with only one alias is to set the call sign to RELAY (with the MYCall command), set the alias to WIDE (with the MYAlias command), and let the Beacon function of the TNC take care of the legal identification requirements. The only negative aspect about using this work-around is that your station icon appears on the APRS maps with a label of RELAY or WIDE rather than your call sign. If you do use this work-around, make sure to include your call sign in the beacon (with the BText command) and to configure the beacon to be sent every ten minutes or less (with Beacon Every command).

Beyond multiple aliases, later advancements in digipeater functionality have promoted further APRS network efficiency.

The WIDEn-n function was added in 1998. When this function is enabled on a network-wide basis, stations can use a path of WIDE3-3, for example, instead of WIDE,WIDE,WIDE, thus promoting network efficiency by having shorter packets (the path is only seven bytes long no matter how many digipeaters are in it).

When a WIDEn-n digipeater receives a packet with a WIDEn-n path, it decrements the –n before it digipeats it. Thus, a WIDE3-3 packet becomes a WIDE3-2 packet when it is initially digipeated. Subsequent digipeats result in WIDE3-1 and WIDE3-0 packets. When –n becomes –0, the packet will not be digipeated.

ARE THERE OTHER WAYS TO SET UP AN APRS DIGIPEATER?

APRS digipeaters come in a variety flavors. Nowhere near the 28 varieties that Howard Johnson's offers, but enough to make things interesting

The original APRS digipeater flavor, as described above, consisted of the requisite radio equipment (transmitter, receiver, antenna, cables and accessories) and a TNC connected to a computer running some version of APRS software. You configure the APRS software, which sets the TNC to act as an APRS digipeater.

The second flavor again consisted of the requisite radio equipment and a TNC connected to a computer. Instead of running some version of APRS software, the computer ran APRS digipeater emulation software. The TNC simply acted as a conduit for packets that it relayed to and from the computer. The APRS digipeater software is called *aprsdigi* and it runs on the *Linux* operating system. Alan Crosswell, N2YGK, created *aprsdigi*.

Kenwood's TM-D700A dual band (144 and 440 MHz) transceiver has a built-in TNC and APRS software, which can be configured as an APRS digipeater without a computer. The necessary configuration can be performed using the controls on the front panel of the radio.

Marco Savegnago, IW3FQG, authored APRS digipeater firmware, called UIDIGI. You replace the firmware in a TNC2 or TNC2 clone with the UIDIGI firmware and the TNC (with the requisite radio equipment) functions as an APRS digipeater. A computer is required to configure the software before burning the EPROM that contains the firmware.

These four flavors of APRS digipeaters have advantages and disadvantages.

THE PROS

The "original" APRS digipeater supports the state-of-the-art WIDEn-n digipeater functions only if those functions are supported by the TNC used with the APRS software. (Current Kantronics TNCs support WIDEn-n.) The APRS software that configures the TNC is available for many computer platforms including *DOS*, *Mac OS*, *Windows*, *Linux*, *Palm OS*, *Unix* and *Windows CE*.

N2YGK's *aprsdigi* supports the WIDEn-n digipeater function.

The TM-D700A is a good choice for emergency communications and public service events because it is self-contained "APRS in a box" and only requires an antenna and power source. It can be up and running very quickly.

UIDIGI supports the WIDEn-n digipeater function. It is a good choice for remote sites because the configuration is permanently stored in memory. Power outages will not affect the configuration, so a computer is not necessary to reconfigure the system. It is also the most inexpensive APRS digipeater flavor because TNC2s and TNC2 clones are plentiful and cheap.

THE CONS

The "original" APRS digipeater does not support WIDEn-n function if that function is not supported by the TNC used with the APRS software. It is not a good choice for a remote site because you need a computer to reconfigure the TNC whenever it loses its configuration due to power outages and such, which are more likely to occur in remote locations.

N2YGK's *aprsdigi* ties up a computer all the time. It also runs on the *Linux* operating system, which is not the most common, friendly or easy-to-learn operating system around.

The TM-D700A does not support the WIDEn-n digipeater functions, therefore, it is not a good choice for a permanent APRS digipeater installation in a network using WIDEn-n.

UIDIGI requires the equipment and the ability to burn EPROMs. Any changes in the digipeater configuration require burning a new EPROM and installing it in the TNC.

N2YGK's *aprsdigi* is available from **ftp://ftp.tapr.org/aprssig/ linux**. UIDIGI is available from **gw.ir3ip.ampr.org/~iw3fqg/files/ UIDIGI/.**

WHAT IS THE RECOMMENDED DIGIPEATER PATH FOR FIXED, NON-DIGIPEATER APRS STATIONS?

Each non-digipeater fixed APRS station should fine-tune its path for compatibility with its local APRS network once it becomes familiar with that network.

Rather than using the generic path of RELAY or WIDE, the path should be set with the call sign of the nearest digipeater that the fixed station uses to get its packets out into the network. In order to minimize duplication of effort, this is especially critical in areas where the fixed APRS station accesses two or more digipeaters with its RELAY or WIDE path.

The preferable path for a fixed station is to use the call sign of the nearest accessible digipeater followed by one or two WIDEs (CALLSIGN,WIDE or CALLSIGN,WIDE,WIDE, or in WIDEn-n APRS networks, CALLSIGN,WIDE1-1 or CALLSIGN,WIDE2-2). In this way, the fixed APRS station gets its packets out of its neighborhood in the most efficient way, that is, directly to one digipeater serving its area (by means of the CALLSIGN portion of its path). Then that digipeater uses the WIDE portion of the path to propagate the packets of the fixed station out into the APRS network via digipeaters with aliases of WIDE.

WHAT IS THE RECOMMENDED DIGIPEATER PATH FOR MOBILE APRS STATIONS?

Ideally, if a mobile APRS station knows the lay of the APRS network that it traverses, it should use the same path rules that apply to fixed APRS stations, that is, the call sign of the nearest accessible digipeater followed by one or two WIDEs (CALLSIGN,WIDE or CALLSIGN,WIDE,WIDE, or in WIDEn-n APRS networks, CALLSIGN,WIDE1-1 or CALLSIGN,WIDE2-2).

Unless the mobile station traverses the same path regularly, it is difficult if not impossible for it to be intimately familiar with the APRS network it passes through. As a result, a different path rule applies to the typical mobile APRS station and that rule is simple: a mobile APRS station should set its path for RELAY,WIDE or

RELAY,WIDE**n-n**, where **n** should be increased when traveling through less populous areas and decreased when traveling through metropolitan areas.

WHAT DIGIPEATER PATHS SHOULD BE AVOIDED?

When configuring your digipeater path, RELAY should only be used in the first slot of your path (RELAY,WIDE, not RELAY,RELAY or WIDE,RELAY). RELAYs are intended to fill the gap to a WIDE, that is, every RELAY should be able to access a WIDE, so a path of RELAY, RELAY is not necessary. A path of WIDE,RELAY makes no sense in any scenario because if you are able to access a WIDE, you have no need for a RELAY, and furthermore, your packets will be heard by all the RELAYs that can hear the WIDE anyway.

Also, avoid using more than two WIDEs in your digipeater path (WIDE,WIDE, not WIDE,WIDE,WIDE). More than two WIDEs cause packet ping-pong with the first WIDE repeating its own packet after it hears it being transmitted by the second WIDE.

On the other hand, a digipeater path of WIDE3-3 is permissible in a WIDEn-n APRS network where call sign substitution is enabled because such a network is designed to prevent packet ping-pong.

WHAT IS THE ADVANTAGE OF APRS SOFTWARE REGISTRATION?

Most versions of APRS are shareware. The philosophy of shareware is that you can try out the software for free to see if it is suitable for you. If you intend to continue using it, then you are obligated to register the software and pay a registration fee.

Unregistered APRS software is not fully functional. It lacks the ability to save its configuration. As a result, you must configure the

The Kenwood
TM-D700A transceiver.

software every time you start it.

When you register APRS software, you receive a registration number that you enter into the software and then it becomes fully functional. (Information on how to register the software is included with each version of APRS.)

Table 4-1

APRS Station Icons and Symbols

Table	Symbol	GPSxyz	Description
/	!	BB	Police, Sheriff
/	"	BC	reserved
/	#	BD	Digipeater (Green Hollow Star)
/	$	BE	Phone
/	%	BF	DX Cluster
/	&	BG	Gateway
/		BH	Aircraft (Small)
/	(	BI	Cloudy
/	)	BJ	
/	*	BK	Snowmobile
/	+	BL	Red Cross
/	,	BM	Boy Scouts
/	-	BN	House, QTH with Vertical Antenna
/	.	BO	X (Small)
/	/	BP	Dot
/	O	PO	Circle (Numbered)
/	1	P1	Circle (Numbered)
/	2	P2	Circle (Numbered)
/	3	P3	Circle (Numbered)
/	4	P4	Circle (Numbered)
/	5	P5	Circle (Numbered)
/	6	P6	Circle (Numbered)
/	7	P7	Circle (Numbered)
/	8	P8	Circle (Numbered)
/	9	P9	Circle (Numbered)
/	:	MR	Fire
/	;	MS	Campground, Tent, Portable
/	<	MT	Motorcycle
/	=	MU	Railroad Engine
/	>	MV	Car
/	?	MW	File Server, Position Server
/	@?	MX	Hurricane, Tropical Storm)
/	A	PA	Aid Station
/	B	PB	BBS
/	C	PC	Canoe
/	D	PD	
/	E	PE	Eyeball
/	F	PF	
/	G	PG	Grid Square (6-digit)
/	H	PH	Hotel (Blue Dot)
/	I	PI	TCP/IP
/	J	PJ	
/	K	PK	School
/	L	PL	
/	M	PM	MacAPRS
/	N	PN	NTS Station
/	O	PO	Balloon
/	P	PP	Police Car

Table	Symbol	GPSxyz	Description
/	Q	PQ	
/	R	PR	Recreation Vehicle
/	S	PS	Space Shuttle
/	T	PT	SSTV
/	U	PU	Bus
/	V	PV	ATV
/	W	PW	National Weather Service Site
/	X	PX	Helicopter
/	Y	PY	Yacht, Sailboat
/	Z	PZ	WinAPRS
/	[	HS	Runner, Jogger
/	\	HT	Triangle (Direction Finding)
/	]	HU	PBBS, Mailbox
/	A	HV	Aircraft (Large)
/	_	HW	Weather Station
/	'	HX	Satellite Ground Station
/	a	LA	Ambulance
/	b	LB	Bicycle
/	c	LC	
/	d	LD	Fire Department
/	e	LE	Horse
/	f	LF	Fire Truck
/	q	LG	Glider, Hang Glider
/	h	LH	Hospital
/	i	LI	Islands on the Air (IOTA)
/	j	LJ	Jeep
/	k	LK	Truck
/	l	LL	
/	m	LM	MIC-Encoder Repeater
/	n	LN	Node
/	o	LO	Emergency Operations Center (EOC)
/	p	LP	Rover, Dog, Puppy
/	q	LQ	Grid Square (4-digit)
/	r	LR	Antenna
/	s	LS	Power Boat
/	t	LT	Truck Stop
/	u	LU	Truck (18-Wheeler)
/	v	LV	Van
/	w	LW	Water Station
/	x	LX	X-APRS (UNIX APRS)
/	y	LY	House, QTH with Yagi Antenna
/	z	LZ	
/	{	J1	
/	l	J2	reserved
/	}	J3	
	~	J3	reserved
\	!	OB	Emergency
\	"	OC	reserved
\	#	OD	Digipeater (Green Numbered Star)
\	$	OE	Bank or ATM

(continued)

Table	Symbol	GPSxyz	Description
\	%	OF	
\	&	OG	Gateway (Numbered Diamond)
\		OH	Crash Site
\	(	OI	Cloudy
\	)	OJ	
\	*	OK	Snow
\	+	OL	Church
\	,	OM	Girl Scouts
\	-	ON	House
\	.	OO	Vicinity Ambiguous Plot
\	/	OP	
\	0	A0	Circle (Numbered)
\	1	A1	
\	2	A2	
\	3	A3	
\	4	A4	
\	5	A5	
\	6	A6	
\	7	A7	
\	8	A8	
\	9	A9	Gas Station
\	:	NR	Driving Hail
\	;	NS	Park, Picnic Area
\	<	NT	Advisory
\	=	NU	
\	>	NV	Car (Numbered)
\	?	NW	Information Kiosk
\	@	NX	Hurricane, Tropical Storm
\	A	AA	Box (Numbered)
\	B	AB	Blowing Snow
\	C	AC	Coast Guard
\	D	AD	Drizzle
\	E	AE	Smoke
\	F	AF	Freezing Rain
\	G	AG	Snow Shower
\	H	AH	Haze
\	I	AI	Rain Shower
\	J	AJ	Lightning
\	K	AK	Kenwood Radio
\	L	AL	Lighthouse
\	M	AM	
\	N	AN	Navigation Buoy
\	O	AO	
\	P	AP	Parking

Table	Symbol	GPSxyz	Description
\	Q	AQ	Earthquake
\	R	AR	Restaurant
\	S	AS	Satellite, Pacsat
\	T	AT	Thunderstorm
\	U	AU	Sunny
\	V	AV	VORTAC Navigational Aid
\	W	AW	National Weather Service Site (Numbered)
\	X	AX	Pharmacy
\	Y	AY	
\	Z	AZ	
\	[	DS	Wall Cloud
\	/	DT	
\	]	DU	
\	A	DV	Aircraft (Numbered)
\		DW	Weather Site (Numbered)
\	῾	DX	Rain
\	a	SA	ARRL, ARES
\	b	SB	Duststorm, Sandstorm
\	c	SC	Civil Defense (RACES) (Numbered)
\	d	SD	DX Spot by Call Sign
\	e	SE	Sleet
\	f	SF	Funnel Cloud
\	g	SG	Gale Flags
\	h	SH	Ham Radio Store
\	i	SI	
\	j	SJ	Work Zone
\	k	SK	
\	l	SL	Area Locations (Box, Circle, etc.)
\	m	SM	Value Signpost, Milepost (3-digit)
\	n	SN	Triangle (Numbered)
\	o	SO	Small Circle
\	p	SP	Partly Cloudy
\	q	SQ	
\	r	SR	Restrooms
\	s	SS	Ship, Boat (Numbered)
\	t	ST	Tornado
\	u	SU	Truck (Numbered)
\	v	SV	Van (Numbered)
\	w	SW	Flooding
\	X	SX	
\	y	SY	
\	Z	Sz	
\	{	Q1	Fog
\	1	Q2	
\	}	Q3	
\	~	Q4	

5

OPERATION

This chapter describes how to use APRS on the air and on the Internet.

WHAT ARE THE COMMON RADIO FREQUENCIES FOR APRS OPERATION?

On VHF, most APRS activity in North America occurs on 2 meters at 144.39 MHz using 1200 bit/s.

On UHF, 445.925 MHz is the focus of UHF APRS activity using 9600 or 1200 bit/s.

On HF, 10.151.51 MHz LSB is the frequency of choice and 300 bit/s is the data rate. Note that the carrier is actually 2125 kHz down from 10.151.51 MHz, so it *is* within the Amateur Radio allocated frequencies.

I START APRS AND ITS MAP FILLS UP WITH DATA. WHAT AM I TO MAKE OF IT ALL?

An APRS map display like that shown in **Figure 5-1** may be a little overwhelming to the novice APRS user, so let us try to get a handle on what we are looking at.

The map is a simple outline map that represents the Eastern Seaboard of the US from the southern tip of Maine to Toms River on the New Jersey shore. The only geographic features represented on this map are state borders, the coastline, major bodies of water, and major highways; everything else you see on the map is APRS-related.

The various symbols on the map represent the various APRS

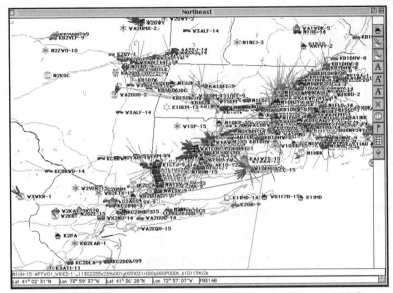

Figure 5-1—Twenty-four hours of APRS activity fills an APRS map.

stations and objects detected by APRS. The vehicle symbols
(automobiles, trucks, jeeps, boats, trains, etc.) represent APRS
stations that are mobile. The building symbols represent APRS
stations that are stationary (home/base stations, emergency
operations centers, hospitals, police stations, etc.) The star
symbols represent APRS digipeaters. The circular "WX"
symbols represent APRS weather stations.

The narrow lines emanating from some vehicle symbols
indicate the course or direction that the vehicle is heading. The
thick lines emanating from the weather stations indicate the
wind direction and relative wind speed (the longer the line, the
higher the wind speed).

The blurs, like the one near the center of the map, represent
moving APRS stations. The blurs are the result of the moving
station's symbol being redisplayed each time its movement is
detected and displayed by APRS.

Redrawing a map eliminates the blurs/multiple symbol
displays and results in a map like that shown in **Figure 5-2**. That
makes the map less cluttered and easier to interpret.

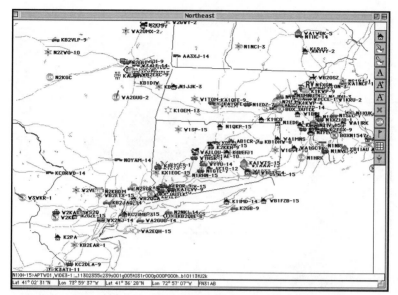

Figure 5-2—A redrawn APRS map eliminates the clutter and redundancy that results in extended periods of APRS activity.

HOW DO I CHANGE THE MAGNIFICATION OF THE MAPS THAT APRS DISPLAYS?

All versions of APRS that use maps permit you to zoom in (magnify) and zoom out of the maps.

Figure 5-3 shows how APRS looks after I start it up at my APRS base station. The software loads the map I selected for startup (an outline map of the northeast corner of the US) and displays it all in one window. This map display is fine for a wide view of APRS activity, but the APRS activity is cluttered and, as a result, the map is not very useful to see what is going on at the local level.

Figure 5-4 shows the result of centering the map on my APRS base station (in west central Connecticut) and zooming in by one level of magnification. This map display is fine for a local view of APRS activity, but it is still too cluttered to clearly pick out each APRS station.

Figure 5-5 shows the result of zooming in the map by two levels of magnification. This is better, but there is still a lot of clutter.

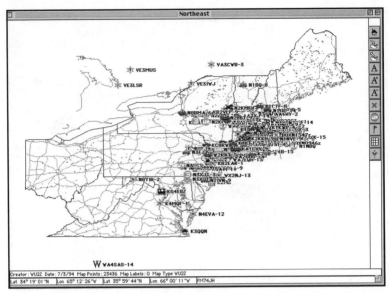

Figure 5-3—Starting up APRS typically results in a map reduced to fill the APRS map window.

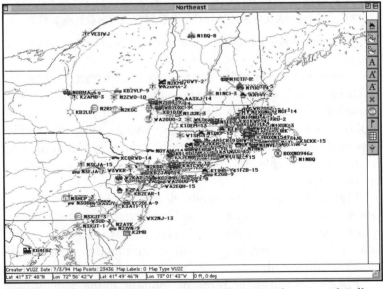

Figure 5-4—APRS allows you to magnify a map for more detail. This is the result of one level of magnification.

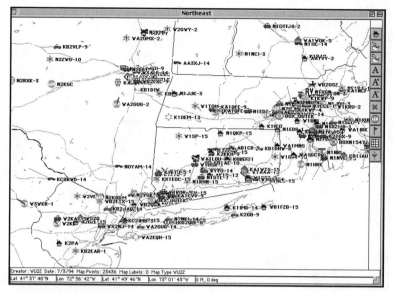

Figure 5-5—Two levels of magnification results in this APRS map display.

Figure 5-6 shows the result of zooming in the map by three levels of magnification. Except where stations are co-located or nearly so, you can differentiate most of the individual APRS stations.

Further magnification is possible. You can continue zooming in on clusters of APRS stations until you can differentiate practically all of them. However, if the APRS stations actually share the same location, no level of magnification will separate the stations. For example, "WA1LOU-85" at the center of the map is actually three APRS stations at the same location: WA1LOU-8, my mobile station parked in my garage and WA1LOU-15, my APRS home station, which is an APRS wide digipeater and APRS weather station, each with their own symbols.

By the way, the Page Down and Page Up keys are used in many APRS applications to zoom in (Page Down) and zoom out (Page Up) of maps.

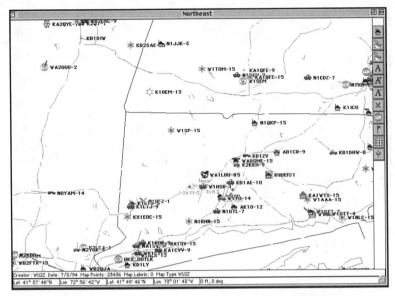

Figure 5-6—Three levels of magnification of this APRS map is just about right to see what is going on at the local level.

HOW DOES APRS TRACK A MOVING OBJECT?

The ability to track moving objects on a map is the primary function (and attraction) of APRS. This function has made APRS an appealing tool for public service communications. The dynamics of tracking public service events require the tracking power of APRS, and the ability to replay the track of a moving object just adds to this power.

Tracking requires the moving object to transmit its position as it traverses its route. This may be accomplished automatically via a GPS receiver configured to the transmitter in the moving object, or manually via operator control. Manual operator control may be performed by an operator inputting position information into a computer running APRS aboard the moving object or remotely by an operator, who placed a moving object like a hurricane on an APRS map. In either case, each time a new position is transmitted for a moving object, the symbol of that object appears in a new position on the APRS map.

Replaying the track of a moving object is performed differently with the various versions of APRS. For example, to replay the track of one object in *APRSdos* or *APRS+SA*, you must select the object before tracking begins. With *MacAPRS*, *WinAPRS* and *X-APRS*, you can select one moving object at any time to replay the entire track of that object only.

Figure 5-7 shows the result of tracking one selected moving object, in this case, K1LTJ-9, a mobile APRS station. K1LTJ-9's track begins at his base station (K1LTJ-5), goes south on Route 7 in Western Connecticut, then makes the return trip north up the same route. The solid overlapping lines along Route 7 indicate the north and south paths of K1LTJ-9 detected by APRS and the automobile symbol near the north end of the path indicates the last position of K1LTJ-9 detected by APRS.

The fields at the bottom of the map display additional information about K1LTJ-9's trip. The fields display the number of packets received from K1LTJ-9 (131), the date and time of

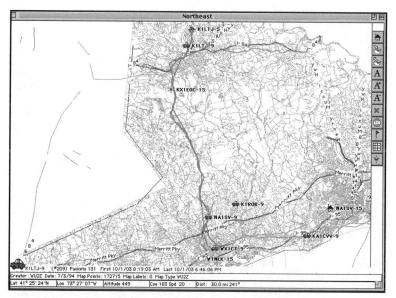

Figure 5-7—This APRS map displays the track of K1LTJ-9 commuting to and from work.

the first received packet (10/01/03, 8:19:03 AM) and the last received packet (10/01/03, 6:46:06 PM). The fields also display the last received position of K1LTJ-9 (41° 25' 24"N, 73° 27' 07"W), altitude (449), course (183), speed (20), and finally, the distance (30.0 mi) and direction (241°) between K1LTJ-9's last received location and the location of the APRS station that was the source of this map (WA1LOU-15).

Figure 5-8 shows the result of tracking multiple moving objects, in this case, all the moving objects detected by APRS. In this display, most of the moving action seems to be taking place on I-84, the route that crosses the map diagonally from the southwest to the northeast.

In addition to displaying tracked objects on maps, APRS also generates a table of tracked objects on command. **Figure 5-9** is an example of a tracked objects table. The table is sorted according to the time. As a result, the last tracked object detected by APRS appears at the top of the table. (The table may be

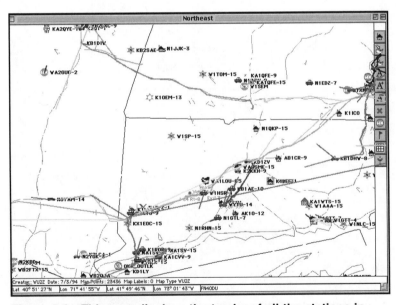

Figure 5-8—This map displays the tracks of all the stations in motion detected by APRS.

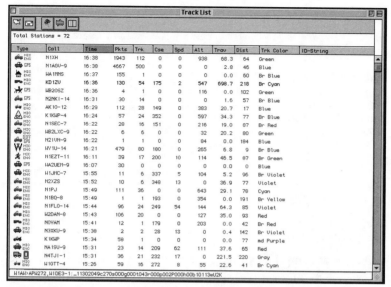

Figure 5-9—The Tracked List of *WinAPRS* **delineates the tracked stations received by your station.**

resorted using the other headings of the table.)

The table displays the following information about each tracked object: type (primary and secondary symbols), call sign and SSID, time of last received packet, number of packets received, number of packets represented by the track, last received course, speed, and altitude, the total distance traveled, the distance to the location of the APRS station that was the source of this table (WA1LOU-15), the color of the track, and the identification text (if any) appended to the object's packets.

HOW DO I SEND AND RECEIVE TEXT MESSAGES WITH APRS?

Sometimes an APRS map itself is not enough and you have to contact another station to pass information concerning activity being displayed on the map. Or you may have a need to pass information to all the stations in the APRS network.

The authors of the APRS protocol foresaw this need and as a result, the software supports communication in real-time. The

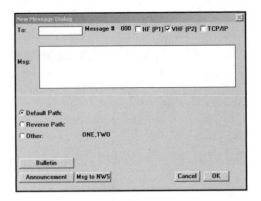

Figure 5-10—You originate an APRS message or bulletin using this window in *WinAPRS*.

software accomplishes this by permitting you to send one-line messages to any active station in the APRS network or by sending multiple-line bulletins to all the stations in the network.

The process of sending and receiving messages varies with each version of APRS. Receiving messages is usually hands-off; whenever you receive a message addressed your station, most versions of APRS automatically display the message. All you have to do is read the message and reply to it if you wish.

Sending a message is a little more involved. Typically, you access a message composition function. **Figure 5-10** represents a typical message composition window. (It is the message composition window of *WinAPRS*, which is virtually the same as the message composition window in *MacAPRS* and *X-APRS*.)

You type the call sign and SSID of the station you wish to contact in the To: field, type the contents of the message in the Msg: field, and send it on its way (by clicking the **OK** button). When the message is received, you receive an acknowledgement of that fact.

HOW DO I MANUALLY ADD AN OBJECT TO AN APRS MAP?

Besides your APRS station, you can add other things to the APRS map and they will appear on all the APRS maps in your network. For example, you can display the path of a hurricane,

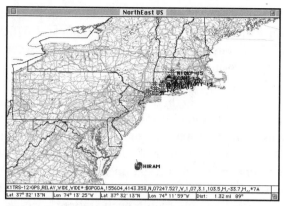

Figure 5-11—The icon of Hurricane Hiram moving up the East Coast is under the control of an APRS station operator.

the lead runner in a marathon, the lead vehicle in a parade, or a mobile communications control center in an emergency or natural disaster scenario.

Let us use the hurricane example. Hurricane Hiram is coming up the coast. You obtain its coordinates, speed and course from the National Weather Service, the Weather Channel or some other reliable source. With this information in hand, you access the add object function of APRS, and input the name, coordinates, speed, and course of the hurricane. You also select an appropriate symbol for the APRS map display (enter the @ in order to display the hurricane symbol). **Figure 5-11** illustrates an object, Hurricane Hiram, that an APRS user placed on a map.

As you receive updates concerning the position, speed and course of Hurricane Hiram, you access APRS and enter the updated information in order to adjust the symbol of the hurricane on the APRS map. And, when the hurricane is over, you access APRS to remove the hurricane symbol from the APRS map.

WHAT STATION INFORMATION DOES APRS COLLECT?

All versions of APRS collect information about the stations

that are active on your APRS network. How they display that information varies between the various versions of APRS.

A list of stations that are active on your APRS network is available in one form or another from most APRS applications. **Figure 5-12** is an example of such a list. It lists the stations received by your station in their order of receipt (the oldest first) and provides the following information concerning each station: primary and secondary map symbols, call sign and SSID, the CAATOFPWDG field, number of packets received, time of first receipt, and contents of identification text (if any).

Each column of the CAATOFPWDG field indicates the following information concerning each station:
- The C column indicates the symbol character.
- The first A column indicates the symbol table.
- The second A column indicates the alarm type, if any.
- The T column indicates the tracked type, if any.
- The O column indicates the object type, if any.

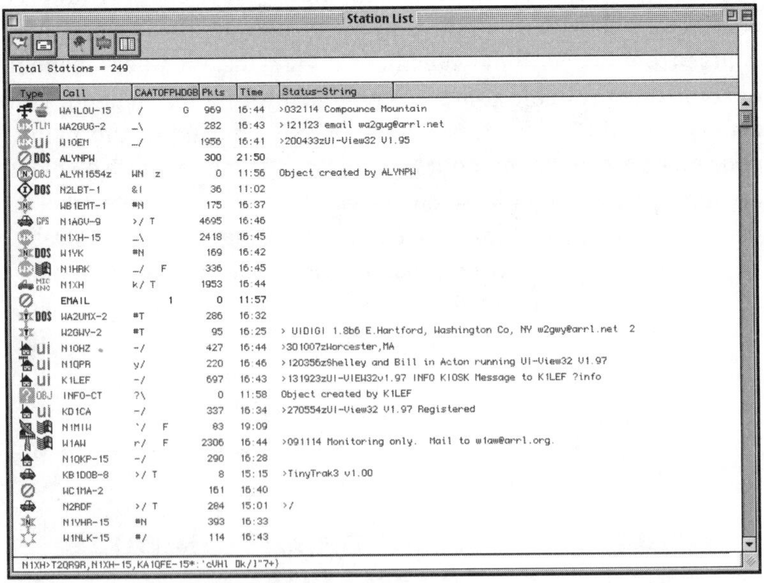

Figure 5-12—The Station List of *Mac/Win/X-APRS* delineates the APRS stations received by your station.

- The F column indicates the flagged type, if any.
- The P column indicates the current count of the message
   pending counter.
- The W column indicates the warning type, if any.
- The D column indicates the danger type, if any.
- The G column indicates the GPS destination, if any.

You can also obtain information about an individual station in APRS. Typically, you select the station whose information you wish to view and APRS displays that information in various ways. For example, **Figure 5-13** is the result of double-clicking your mouse on the symbol of a station displayed on a *MacAPRS* map.

The window displays the station's primary and secondary map symbols, call sign and SSID, number of packets received, date and time of first and last receipt, last received location (latitude and longitude), number of messages sent, and contents of status, identification, and beacon text (if any), actual contents of last received packet, and distance from your APRS station.

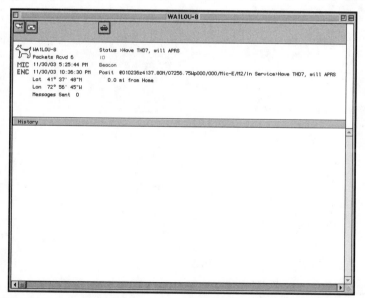

Figure 5-13—APRS displays a variety of information concerning individual APRS stations.

The History panel in the lower half of the window displays all the packets received from the selected station.

Clicking the automobile symbol button reveals additional information, which appears in the upper right panel of the window, as shown in **Figure 5-14**. This information refers to the track of the station (if any) and includes the following data: the number of packets received that compose the track, the distance of the track from beginning to end, the total distance traveled, the current speed and altitude, and the maximum speed and altitude achieved during the track. In this example, notice the anomaly of 0.3 miles distance start-to-finish vs. 76.2 miles distance traveled. The explanation is simple: in this example, APRS tracked a trip totaling 76.2 miles whose starting point and ending point were 0.3 miles apart.

Clicking the balloon symbol button graphically represents the various altitudes that the station reported during its trip, as shown in **Figure 5-15**. This view was originally intended for

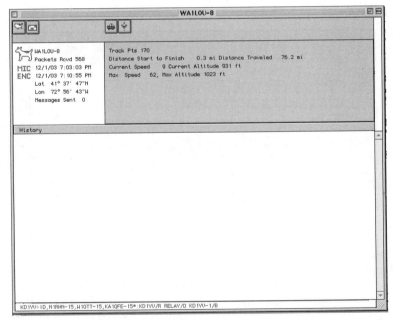

Figure 5-14—APRS also displays information regarding the track of individual APRS stations that are in motion.

tracking APRS stations aboard balloons, but may be used for any moving APRS station. (By the way, that track represents two roundtrips between my home and the salt mine and yes, the trip home does seem as steep as the graph indicates especially during a snowstorm.)

All versions of APRS provide a way of viewing the digipeater path of the APRS stations received by your station. **Figure 5-16** is an example of such a list. It includes the call sign (and SSID) and digipeater path of each station. An asterisk (*) next to the call sign indicates that you received the packets directly from that station, not via a digipeater. An asterisk next to a digipeater indicates that you received the station from that digipeater.

All versions of APRS permit you to display a list of the packets received by your station. **Figures 5-17** and **5-18** respectively illustrate the view packets displays of *APRSdos* and

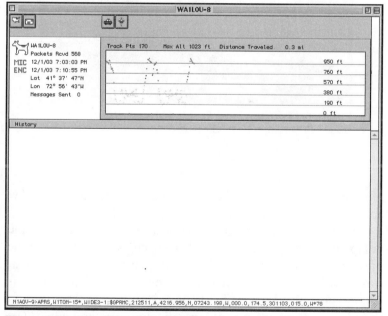

Figure 5-15—The changing altitude of a moving object is displayed graphically by APRS.

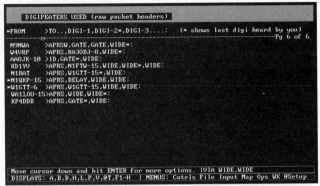

```
   DIGIPEATERS USED (raw packet headers)
*FROM    >TO..,DIGI-1,DIGI-2*,DIGI-3....:  (* shows last digi heard by you)
                                                              ──Pg 6 of 6
N9NWA    >APRSW,GATE,GATE,WIDE*:
W4URP    >APRS,KA3ODJ-8,WIDE*:
AA8JK-10 >ID,GATE*,WIDE:
KD1YV    >APRS,N1FTW-15,WIDE,WIDE*,WIDE:
N1RAT    >APRS,W1GTT-15*,WIDE:
*N1QKP-15 >APRS,RELAY,WIDE,WIDE:
*W1GTT-6 >APRS,W1GTT-15,WIDE,WIDE:
WA1LOU-15>APRS,WIDE,WIDE*:
KP4DDB   >APRS,GATE*,WIDE:




Move cursor down and hit ENTER for more options. !VIA WIDE,WIDE
DISPLAYS: A,B,D,H,L,P,V,@T,F1-H  ! MENUS: Cntrls File Input Map Ops WX @Setup
```

Figure 5-16—The Digipeater List of *APRSdos* lists the digipeaters used by the APRS stations received at your station.

```
                                    At 1227  ToGo:B6m P6m O6m M15




*** LAST 12 packets in VIEW BUFFER:
N2SF>APRS,KD1DU-15*,WIDE,WIDE:N2ZRC    :Why does KD1DU use 3 wides??{2

N2ZRC>APRS,KD1DU-15*,WIDE,WIDE:N2SF    :ack2

N2ZRC>APRS,KD1DU-15,WIDE*,WIDE:N2SF    :ack2

N2SF>APRS,KD1DU-15,WIDE*,WIDE:N2ZRC    :Why can I digipt via kd1du-15, but not

N2ZRC>APRS,KD1DU-15,WIDE,WIDE*:N2SF    :ack2

N2ZRC>APRS,KD1DU-15*,WIDE,WIDE:N2SF    :ack3

N2ZRC>APRS,KD1DU-15,WIDE*,WIDE:N2SF    :ack3

VIEW MODE! Colors show results of APRS parsing.  CANCEL WITH ANY OTHER SCREEN.
```

Figure 5-17—The View Packets list of *APRSdos* displays the last 12 packets received.

MacAPRS. (The *WinAPRS* and *X-APRS* versions of this display are very similar to the *MacAPRS* version of this display.)

Some versions of APRS have a function that lists the number of packets received per hour from each station over the previous 24-hour period. *APRSdos* presents this data in a tabular format, while *MacAPRS*, *WinAPRS*, and *X-APRS* presents this data graphically. **Figures 5-19** and **5-20** illustrate the *APRSdos* and *MacAPRS* versions of the display, respectively. (The *WinAPRS* and *X-APRS* versions of this display are very similar

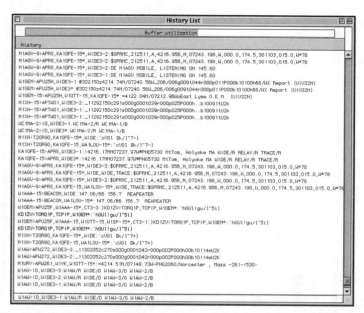

Figure 5-18—The History List of *MacAPRS* **lists all the packets received by your station.**

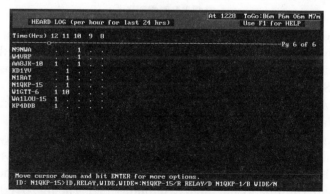

Figure 5-19—The Heard Log of *APRSdos* **lists the number of packets received each hour in a tabular format.**

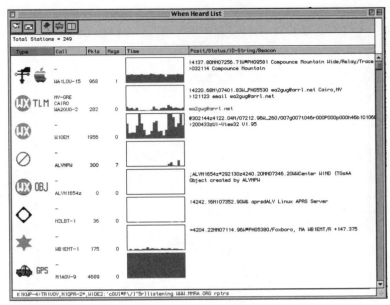

Figure 5-20—The When Heard List of *MacAPRS* lists the number of packets received each hour graphically.

to the *MacAPRS* version of this display.)

WHAT WEATHER INFORMATION DOES APRS COLLECT?

Most versions of APRS collect weather information from the weather stations that are active on your APRS network. How they display that information varies between the various versions of APRS.

Most versions of APRS display weather data next to each weather station that appears on its maps. **Figure 5-21** is an example of such a display. The weather data in this display of the area around Lake Michigan includes temperature, wind speed (MPH), wind gusts (MPH), rainfall (inches), atmospheric pressure (millibars) and relative humidity (%). The line overlaid on the weather station symbol indicates the direction of the wind. A counter indicates the age of the data (in minutes).

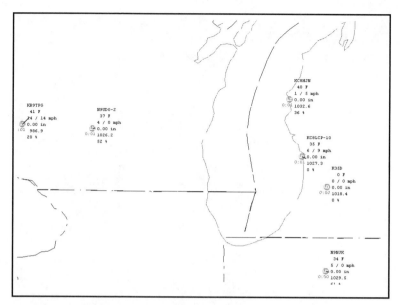

Figure 5-21—APRS weather station data is displayed on APRS maps.

A list of weather stations that are active on your APRS network is available in one form or another from some APRS applications. **Figure 5-22** is an example of such a list. It lists the following information concerning each weather station: primary and secondary map symbol, call sign and SSID, day of the month and time of last packet received, temperature (degrees Fahrenheit), rainfall during previous hour (inches), rainfall during previous day (inches), relative humidity (%), atmospheric pressure (millibars), wind speed (mph), wind gusts (mph), wind direction (degrees), number of alarms generated by the station, distance (miles) and direction (degrees) from your station, and brand of weather station equipment.

Some versions of APRS also display weather data from individually selected weather stations. **Figure 5-23** displays N1HRK's weather data textually, while **Figure 5-24** displays the same information graphically. In both views, wind speed, air temperature, barometric pressure and rainfall are displayed.

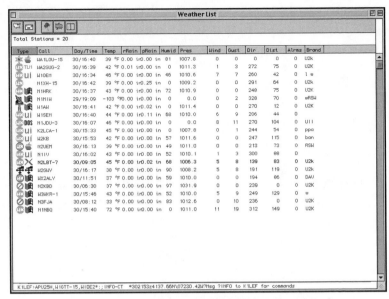

Figure 5-22—The Weather List of *MacAPRS* delineates the
weather data received from the APRS weather stations.

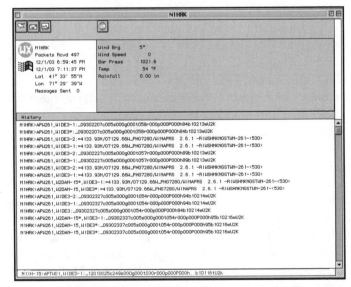

Figure 5-23—APRS permits you to display the weather data from
individual APRS weather stations in a textual format.

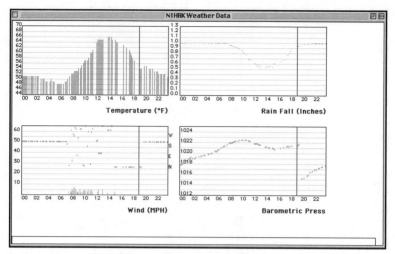

Figure 5-24—A graphical display of weather data from individual APRS stations is also possible with APRS.

DOES APRS DISPLAY ALL THE MAP SYMBOLS THAT IT USES?

Some versions of APRS allow you to view all the symbols that may be used to represent stations and objects on its maps. **Figure 5-25** illustrates all the map symbols available in APRS, their keyboard equivalents and names.

HOW DOES APRS INTERFACE WITH THE INTERNET?

Some APRS stations (called "IGates" for Internet gateways) are connected to the Internet in order to relay the APRS data they receive locally to central Internet sites called APRServers. The APRServers massage this data (deleting bad and duplicate packets), and then allow other stations to access that data in order to view APRS activity worldwide.

If the computer you use for running APRS is connected to the Internet, you can connect to an APRServer and display international APRS activity on your APRS maps. **Figure 5-26** shows a *WinAPRS* map of the Continental US filled with APRS activity after connecting the software to an APRServer via the Internet.

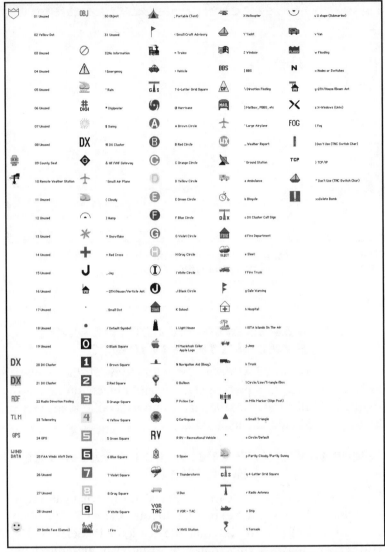

Figure 5-25—Here are all the map symbols available in APRS.

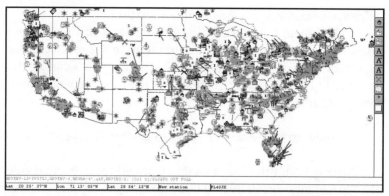

Figure 5-26—Connecting APRS software to an APRServer via the Internet results in a map filled with APRS activity from coast-to-coast.

This virtual APRS window has the same capabilities as an RF-originated APRS window. For example, you can send one-line messages to APRS stations in the virtual APRS window in the same way that you send messages to APRS stations over the local RF APRS network.

By the way, if you connect your APRS software to an APRServer while it is also connected to your APRS station, there will be an intermingling of Internet-originated and RF-originated stations and objects on your APRS maps. You will not be able to differentiate between them, but that does not matter because you can interact with both the Internet-originated and RF-originated APRS stations in the same way.

Also, you can configure your APRS software to permit it to feed your local activity to the Internet; thus, your station becomes an IGate, too.

HOW CAN I SEND E-MAIL VIA APRS?

In addition to giving you the capability to view worldwide APRS activity, IGates permit you to originate one-line e-mail messages to legitimate Internet addresses. After properly addressing the message and transmitting it on the air, any IGate that receives it (and is properly configured to relay it) relays it to the Internet. After the relay, the IGate sends an acknowledgment over the air to the originating station.

To originate a message, simply address it to EMAIL and insert the Internet address as the first item in the message. For example, to send e-mail to n1ed@arrl.net, you address the message to EMAIL and the contents of the message would look something like this:

n1ed@arrl.net Are you going to Dayton this year?

After transmitting the message, you will receive a message like "Email message delivered OK" from any IGate that handles it. Yes—this implies that more than one IGate will relay it to the Internet, but I think you will agree that is a small price to pay for this capability.

IS THERE A DATABASE THAT STORES ALL THIS APRS INFORMATION?

Since the late 1990s, the APRS Internet system has been up and running collecting APRS data from around the world to link all the local RF APRS networks into a single real-time wide-area network. The system handles approximately 300,000 packets a day. Since late 2000, there has been a system in place for long-term storage of the APRS packets.

By querying the APRS database, you can obtain pertinent data concerning APRS activity. For example, I use the system almost every day. After I arrive at the salt mine, I check the system to see if the APRS tracker in my land barge is working. If it is working, my tracker progress from home to the salt mine appears on the maps created from the data stored by the APRS database.

Anybody can access the data, but to facilitate access, a handful of hams have created Web pages that allow you to query the database via a user-friendly interface. **Figure 5-27** shows an example of such a page, i.e., Brian Riley's, N1BQ's APRS Search Page (**www.wulfden.org/APRSQuery.shtml**), which has been up and running for a long time and is a favorite destination for folks wishing to access the database.

Entering the call sign and SSID of an APRS station in the

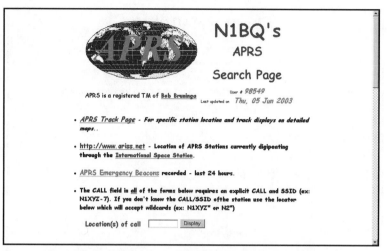

Figure 5-27—Brian Riley's, N1BQ's APRS Search Page accesses the Internet APRS database to find you an APRS station.

"Location(s) of call" field of N1BQ's APRS Search Page causes it to access the database and extract the pertinent data that results in the creation of maps displaying the APRS station's last reported location. As shown in the accompanying **Figures 5-28** through **5-30**, N1BQ's APRS Search Page displays three maps that indicate the location of the station you asked about. A local street-level map covers an approximately 0.5 by 1 mile area, a city- and town-level map covers approximately 25 by 50 miles, and a regional map covers approximately 200 by 400 miles.

The page indicates when the last packet was received from that station and the course and speed of that station—if it was in motion, that is, like an APRS tracker. The page also displays the station's distance and direction from the nearest city, the contents of the station's status packet and the contents of the last raw packet received from that station. Links on the page allow you to access a list of stations near the station of interest. They also allow you to display a US Geological Survey topographical map and an aerial photo, if available, that covers approximately the same area as the local street-level map.

In addition to station location and tracks, you can also

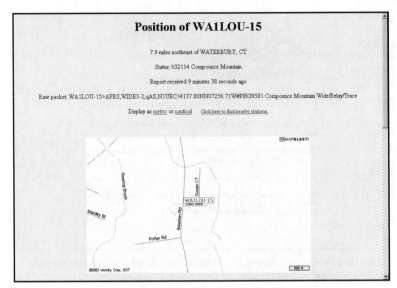

Figure 5-28—The location of an APRS station extracted from the Internet APRS database is displayed on a local street-level map.

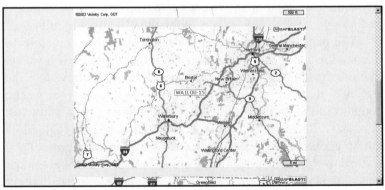

Figure 5-29—The location of an APRS station extracted from the Internet APRS database is also displayed on a city- and town-level map.

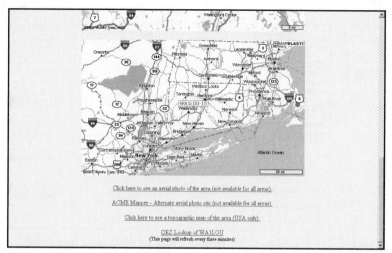

Figure 5-30—A regional map is also used to display the location of an APRS station extracted from the Internet APRS database.

display messages sent to or from a particular station, find APRS stations near another station, near a specific ZIP code, near a specific latitude and longitude, during a specific time period, etc. Also, current weather information and weather history from specific APRS weather stations may be viewed. Raw packet data from any APRS station may also be viewed. **Figures 5-31** and **5-32** show the variety of options that you can use to access the database.

DESCRIBE SOME PRACTICAL USES OF THE APRS INTERNET SYSTEM?

Practical Use 1

A ham posted a message on the Tucson Amateur Packer Radio (TAPR) APRSSIG e-mail list asking if anyone had received any position packets from the APRS station installed in his vehicle. It seems that his vehicle was stolen and if the perpetrators happened to turn on the station equipment, the position packets might help locate the vehicle.

Another ham suggested checking the APRS database to see

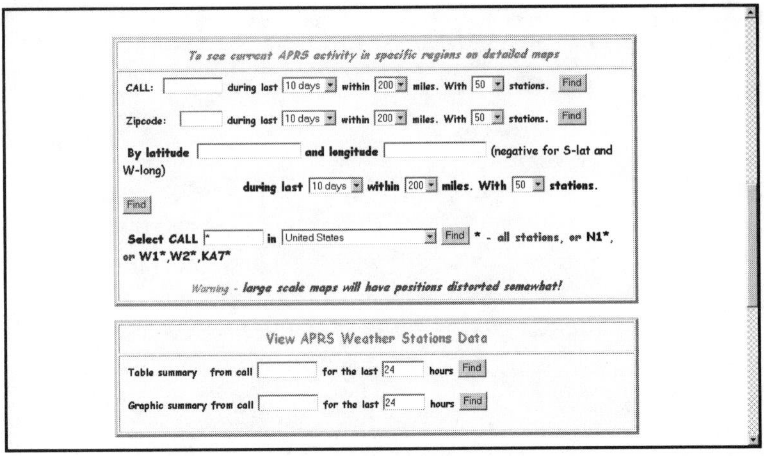

Figure 5-31—N1BQ's APRS Search Page permits you to extract APRS information from the Internet APRS database in a number of ways.

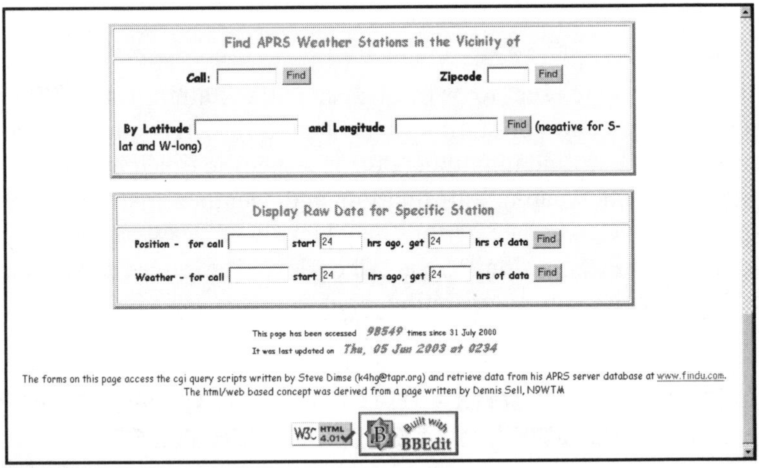

Figure 5-32—Here are still more ways of extracting APRS information from the Internet APRS database courtesy of N1BQ's APRS Search Page.

if his mobile APRS station's position packets had been relayed to the Internet. After checking, he discovered that one of his station's position packets was indeed relayed to the Internet. This clue led the authorities to the location revealed by the position packet and resulted in the arrest of the perpetrators and the recovery of various items of stolen property.

Practical Use 2

I drive my land barge to and from the Dayton Hamvention every spring. I don't own a cell phone because I believe cell phones are a product of the Evil Empire. As a result, I am not on the phone calling home to let the family know that I did not get lost in Akron during the trip. However, the family keeps track of my whereabouts for free by accessing N1BQ's APRS Search Page (**www.wulfden.org/APRSQuery.shtml**) and asking, "Where's WA1LOU-8?" Yes, you do not have to have an Amateur Radio license to access the APRS database, so let your family and friends in on the fun.

Practical Use 3

I live on a hill and work in a valley. The two locations are only 19 miles apart, but the weather conditions can be very different between the two sites. In the winter, it may be raining

WA1LOU-15 Weather Reports

Display with metric or nautical units.

time (UTC)	temp F	wind direction	speed MPH	gust MPH	rain 1hr in	rain 24hr in	rain mm in	humidity %	barometer mm Hg
20031202200802	25	323	2.0	10.0	0.00	0.00	0.00	61	1015.4
20031202195939	26	1	1.0	6.0	0.00	0.00	0.00	59	1015.3
20031202194958	26	295	5.0	13.0	0.00	0.00	0.00	56	1015.2
20031202193528	27	1	7.0	13.0	0.00	0.00	0.00	56	1014.9
20031202193003	28	285	6.0	18.0	0.00	0.00	0.00	56	1014.8
20031202192032	28	301	9.0	16.0	0.00	0.00	0.00	55	1014.6
20031202190136	28	290	7.0	17.0	0.00	0.00	0.00	60	1014.4
20031202185158	27	231	6.0	18.0	0.00	0.00	0.00	65	1014.2
20031202183728	28	288	10.0	22.0	0.00	0.00	0.00	65	1014.1
20031202182748	29	353	8.0	16.0	0.00	0.00	0.00	67	1013.9
20031202181404	28	316	4.0	13.0	0.00	0.00	0.00	72	1013.7
20031202180827	28	292	4.0	14.0	0.00	0.00	0.00	75	1013.6
20031202175947	29	308	6.0	16.0	0.00	0.00	0.00	77	1013.7
20031202175358	29	285	6.0	14.0	0.00	0.00	0.00	78	1013.6
20031202174531	28	308	5.0	15.0	0.00	0.00	0.00	81	1013.6
20031202173118	28	280	9.0	14.0	0.00	0.00	0.00	83	1013.6
20031202172457	29	315	2.0	8.0	0.00	0.00	0.00	81	1013.2
20031202171701	30	276	2.0	10.0	0.00	0.00	0.00	77	1013.3
20031202170540	32	302	11.0	21.0	0.00	0.00	0.00	62	1012.6
20031202165558	32	283	9.0	18.0	0.00	0.00	0.00	61	1012.4

Figure 5-33—This Web page accesses the Internet APRS database to extract and display data from an APRS weather station.

at work, but snowing at home. A few times, I have left work at the end of the day driving through a light shower only to find six inches of snow at the top of the hill (assuming that I make it to the top of the hill with the balding all-weather tires that I have on the land barge).

I have a fully outfitted APRS weather station at home and it would be nice to be able to access it from work to know which way the snow blows on those winter days when it is raining at the salt mine. But I cannot access my weather station from work because the APRS radio in the land barge is one that does not display weather data from APRS weather stations.

Instead of buying a new radio, I built a simple Web site (**www.tapr.org/~wa1lou/wx.html**) that accesses the APRS database, extracts my weather station's data, and displays it on a Web page in tabular format, as shown in **Figure 5-33**, and a graphical format, as shown in **Figure 5-34**. Now, I can access

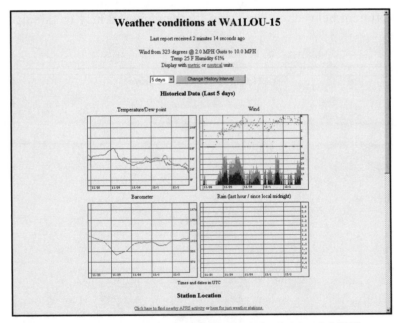

Figure 5-34—Another Web page accesses the Internet APRS database to extract the same data from an APRS weather station, but displays it in a graphical format.

my weather station using the computer on my desk at the salt mine.

HOW CAN I USE APRS TO CHASE DX?

Two meters is open this morning. There is a tropospheric (or "tropo") inversion along the East Coast that is enhancing propagation out to a range of 100-200 miles. You would never know this by monitoring the 2-meter SSB calling frequency as there is nary a signal to be heard there. So, how do I know that 2 meters is open? APRS is showing the way.

Long before the marriage of home computers and Amateur Radio led me into the ham radio digital dimension, my main interest was in the VHF/UHF world. One of my first radios was a Heathkit 2-meter Benton Harbor Lunchbox, also known as a "Twoer." It was a one-channel AM transceiver with a superregenerative receiver. "Super" was a misnomer. It certainly was not of Clark Kent's lineage as it left a lot to be desired in the selectivity department. It was so non-selective that one strong signal seemed to fill the whole 2-meter band!

But, due to my limited college income (or should I say "superincome"), I used to haul my Twoer around in my car looking for the high spots in New Haven County, Connecticut, trying to work 2-meter DX. It was tough going, but I managed to work a handful of states because the receiver was sensitive, albeit non-selective.

Then came FM, but I won't get into that. Anyway, the VHF/UHF bug bit me a long time ago and I still chase 2-meter DX whenever it is available.

Propagation Tool Time

When I started playing with APRS, I thought that it might be a suitable tool for chasing 2-meter DX. Since most APRS activity occurs on the same channel (for example, 144.39 MHz on 2 meters), if you continuously monitor that channel, you can tell that the band is open when stations begin appearing on your APRS map that don't normally appear there.

I was sold on using APRS as a 2-meter propagation alerting mechanism when one July afternoon, stations in Georgia started popping up on my APRS map. I guessed that sporadic E propagation was in the works, so I switched to SSB and worked a number of stations in Florida for my 26th state on 2 meters.

The outer limits of my APRS coverage area during normal 2-meter propagation conditions is WA2JNF in Brooklyn, 85 miles to my southeast and W1TDG in Hinsdale, New Hampshire, 90 miles to my northeast. However, the morning I wrote this, my computer monitor displayed stations such as WA1YKN on Cape Cod, 135 miles to my east, NR1N in Warner, New Hampshire, 133 miles to my northeast, and N2MSM on the South Jersey shore, 174 miles to my southeast, indicating that there was tropo inversion propagation.

Wheat vs. Chaff

To use this tool correctly, you must correctly interpret what your APRS map is displaying. On a typical day, an APRS map displays a lot of stations within a 150-mile radius of your station as well as pockets of activity scattered across the continent. Such a display does not necessarily mean that the band is open.

Most of the stations within a 150-mile radius (give or take mileage depending on the lay of your APRS LAN) are displayed on your map because APRS digipeaters are relaying their positions to your station. Similarly, the stations beyond the 150-mile radius are likely to be HF APRS stations whose positions are being relayed to 2 meters by an APRS HF gateway station on your APRS LAN. In any case, you are not receiving most of these stations directly; repeaters and gateways are doing the work. Only when you receive a distant station directly is it an indication of unusual propagation conditions. So, how do you differentiate the directly received stations from the digipeated and gatewayed stations?

Various versions of APRS allow you to filter out all but the direct stations. For example, invoking the Controls-Filters-Direct series of commands in *APRSdos* will only display the stations you hear directly. Display>Station Display Mode/ Options>Direct Stations Only does the same in *MacAPRS*, *WinAPRS* and *X-APRS*.

After you have used APRS for a while, you get a feel for

which stations are within your normal outer limits, as well as the HF stations that are normally being gatewayed to your LAN. When an unfamiliar station appears on your map, you can check how you are receiving it by using commanding APRS to display its path. For example, today the path of N1HRK in Candia, New Hampshire appears as K1HJC>APRS,NR1N-2,WIDE.

This indicates that I am receiving K1HJC directly. An asterisk in the path would indicate otherwise. For example, if an asterisk followed NR1N-2 or WIDE, it would indicate that I was receiving K1HJC via digipeater NR1N-2 or via a digipeater with an alias of WIDE. Similarly, if GATE* appeared in the path, it would indicate that the station was being gatewayed to me.

That explains how you can use APRS as a VHF/UHF propagation tool. Now let me go and look at my APRS map. Maybe I can work state number 27!

6
TECHNICAL SUPPORT

Technical support for APRS is available via the Internet at a variety of Web sites and e-mail lists. The following paragraphs list the sites and e-mail lists devoted to the current releases of APRS software.

WEB SITES

The following Web sites provide a variety of information and technical support for the various flavors of APRS software.

APRS/CE: **www.tapr.org/~aprsce/**

APRS+SA: **www.tapr.org/~kh2z/aprsplus/**

APRSdos: **web.usna.navy.mil/~bruninga/aprs.html**

APRSPoint: **www.aprspoint.com/**

MacAPRS: **aprs.rutgers.edu/**

The *UI-View* home page on the Web.

APRS+SA's Web site.

pocketAPRS: **www.pocketaprs.com/**
UI-View: **www.peak-systems.com/**
WinAPRS: **aprs.rutgers.edu/**
X-APRS: **aprs.rutgers.edu/**
XASTIR: **www.xastir.org/**

E-MAIL LISTS

UI-View has a support and discussion Yahoo Groups e-mail list. To subscribe, go to **groups.yahoo.com/group/ui-view/join**.

XASTIR has e-mail lists for users and developers. To subscribe to the users' list, go to **krypton.hscs.virginia.edu/ mailman/listinfo/xastir**. To subscribe to the developers' list, go to **krypton.hscs.virginia.edu//mailman/listinfo/xastir-dev**.

Tucson Amateur Packet Radio (TAPR) sponsors the following e-mail lists devoted to supporting APRS.

APRSNEWS distributes announcements concerning new releases of APRS software.

APRSPLUS is devoted to *APRS+SA*.

APRSSAT is devoted to the discussion of using APRS with Amateur Radio satellites.

APRSSIG is intended for the discussion of all APRS topics.

APRSSPEC is intended for the discussion of the APRS

protocol documentation project.

HTAPRS is devoted to the discussion of APRS topics related to the Kenwood TH-D7 handheld transceiver.

MIC-E is intended for the discussion of the MIC-E module.

PROPNET is devoted to an ongoing VHF propagation experiment using APRS.

To subscribe to any of these lists, go to **www.tapr.org/ cgi-bin/lyris.pl?site=tapr**.

AFTERWORD

Steve Dimse, K4HG, the "father of the Internet face of APRS," graciously agreed to write the Afterword of this book.

Over the last 10 years, APRS has gone from nothing more than a good idea to being one of Amateur Radio's largest, most innovative and fastest growing cultures. For the last 5 years, I've been hearing people say that APRS has peaked. So far, the naysayers have been wrong, and I think APRS still has its brightest moments ahead. Predicting the future is always a risky proposition, especially in something a durable as a book, but here are some of the possibilities I see in APRS over the next few years.

So far, the focus of APRS has been on getting information from mobile users to central sites, whether a command post, EOC, base station, or the Internet and **www.findU.com**. A big change I see coming is more focus on getting various forms of information to the mobile user. The possibilities are legion... my personal interest is in personalized weather data, but other possibilities include visitor information, traffic information, driving directions, local repeaters, and so forth. The Internet is a great source of this kind of information and more and more of it will become available to APRS users.

We have already seen a proliferation of client programs, but so far, they are more alike than different. There will be more specialization within the various APRS programs to suit the varied interests of the users. In addition, there will be more modularization of those programs, allowing users to choose the features they care about without being burdened by features they do not want or need.

The RF infrastructure is overdue for a big overhaul; most areas with more than a few APRS users are experiencing

1

congestion on 144.39 MHz. A large part of the future of APRS depends on increasing the effective bandwidth to the users in the field. A lot of ideas have been thrown around, most involving using high-speed packet or the Internet as a backbone. Over the next couple of years, I expect to see some of these ideas developed into test systems and hopefully one or more will function well enough that it can be rolled out into general usage.

APRS-now exists as it does because of the actions of a very small number of people, each of who has shaped APRS in very personal ways. Likewise, the world of APRS-future depends almost completely on who steps forward to make things happen. You just cannot predict who is in the shadows is just about to step into the limelight... maybe you?

Steve Dimse, K4HG

APPENDIX A

COMMANDS

The following tables list and briefly describe all the commands in the five versions of APRS software and the Kenwood TH-D7 transceiver APRS mode.

APRS (DOS)

You choose most *APRS (DOS)* commands by typing the uppercase characters of the command name. For example, to select the Positions command, you type the letter P; to select the Controls > Filters > dX command, you type C, then F, then X. A few *APRS (DOS)* commands are selected by typing a number (e.g., 9), pressing a control-character (e.g., [Home]), or pressing a function-key (e.g., [F5]).

Some *APRS (DOS)* commands use the control character [Alt-S]. To enter this control character, hold down the Control [Alt] key and press the S key.

Keyboard Command

Description [default, if any]

Keyboard Command	Description [default, if any]
[	display more map labels
[Alt-S] > Df > dfJr	turn on/off DFjr mode [off]
[Alt-S] > Df > Dfsp	turn on/off DFSP mode [off]
[Alt-S] > Df > Magnetic_variation	turn on/off for magnetic DF bearings and headings [off]
[Alt-S] > Formats > Compressed	turn on/off packet compression mode [off]
[Alt-S] > Formats > Grid_in_to	turn on/off grid-in-to mode [off]
[Alt-S] > Formats > Meteor_scatter	turn on/off meteor scatter mode [off]
[Alt-S] > Formats > Normal	turn on/off normal APRS operation [on]
[Alt-S] > Formats > Space	turn on/off spacecraft mode [off]
[Alt-S] > Gps > Dgps	select Differential GPS mode
[Alt-S] > Gps > Modes > Arnav	select ARNAV GPS mode
[Alt-S] > Gps > Modes > Both_gga/rmc	select both the GGA and RMC sentence format GPS modes
[Alt-S] > Gps > Modes > Esp	select E^ Single Port (ESP) GPS mode
[Alt-S] > Gps > Modes > Gga	select GGA sentence format GPS mode
[Alt-S] > Gps > Modes > Hsp	select GPS Hardware Single Port mode
[Alt-S] > Gps > Modes > Klynas	configure APRS (DOS) to use Klynas Engineering's Streets-On-Disk
[Alt-S] > Gps > Modes > My$	select MY$ GPS mode
[Alt-S] > Gps > Modes > NMEA_log	turn on/off saving NMEA data to a file [off]
[Alt-S] > Gps > Modes > Rmc	select the RMC sentence format GPS mode
[Alt-S] > Gps > Modes > Spm	select GPS Single Port Mode
[Alt-S] > Gps > Off/on_gps	disable SPM or HSP
[Alt-S] > Gps > Plot	display plot of GPS satellites and their signal strengths
[Alt-S] > Gps > Time_sync	set system clock from local NMEA/GPS equipment
[Alt-S] > Gps > Waypoints	send waypoints to GPS

[Alt-S] > Modes > alt_Net	turn on/off special function net mode [off]
[Alt-S] > Modes > Auto_space	turn on/off automatic spacecraft mode [off]
[Alt-S] > Modes > Master	configure computer as the master in a Zip LAN
[Alt-S] > Modes > Out_new_gga	output GGA-formatted position packet upon receipt of new position
[Alt-S] > Modes > Special	turn on/off special event mode [off]
[Alt-S] > Modes > Zip_lan	configure the computer for a LAN where multiple computers share one TNC
[Alt-S] > Other > Above_avg_terrain	enter the height above average terrain (HAAT) of your station
[Alt-S] > Other > Beeps	turn on/off APRS sound [on]
[Alt-S] > Other > Dst	turn on/off Daylight Saving Time clock setting
[Alt-S] > Other > Ega	turn on/off EGA monitor operation [off]
[Alt-S] > Other > Game	play chess with APRS (DOS)
[Alt-S] > Other > Lock	lock computer keyboard
[Alt-S] > Other > Midnight_save	save all APRS (DOS) files at midnight
[Alt-S] > Other > Redraw	select rate of screen redraw
[Alt-S] > Other > Screen_saver	enables/disables screen saver function [off]
[Alt-S] > Other > Zone	change time zone of your station
[Alt-S] > Ports > Dual_ports	configure software for connection to dual-port TNC
[Alt-S] > Ports > Modem_remote	configure software for connection to a telephone-line modem
[Alt-S] > Ports > Single_port	configure software for connection to single-port TNC
[Alt-S] > Rates	select display and sending rates for GPS, weather and direction finding data
[Alt-S] > Save	save current map and configuration
[Alt-S] > Tnc	configure TNC with TNC APRS parameters

[Alt-T]	display received telemetry data
[Delete]	deselect (unhook) an object
[Down Arrow]	move cursor down
[End]	center map on the default location of your station
[Enter]	select (hook) an object
[Escape]	move cursor to center of map
[F1]	display APRS (DOS) help
[F10]	turn on/off Windows mode [off]
[F2]	compose and transmit reply to last received message
[F3]	display more map labels
[F4]	display fewer map labels
[F5]	enter fade point for omni-directional direction finding
[F6]	configure the speed of your mobile station to 0
[F7]	select low (23-line) or high (43-line) resolution display [low]
[F8]	plot an immediate fix in GPS/HSP mode
[F9]	adjust map size to display all stations
[Home]	center map at current cursor position
[Insert]	move selected (hooked) object
[Left Arrow]	move cursor left
[Page Down]	magnify map
[Page Up]	reduce map magnification
[Right Arrow]	move cursor right
[Space Bar]	display/redraw currently selected map
[Tab]	display status of Control and Setup command parameters

[Up Arrow]	move cursor up
]	display fewer map labels
1	display default map
3	display map saved for key 3
5	display map saved for key 5
7	display map saved for key 7
9	display map saved for key 9
All	display all received messages and beacons in chronological order
Bulletins	display last 22 received bulletins
Controls > Bands > 2_port	configure APRS (DOS) for dual-port TNC operation
Controls > Bands > Hf	configure APRS (DOS) for HF TNC operation
Controls > Bands > Vhf	configure APRS (DOS) for VHF/UHF TNC operation
Controls > Cw > Disable	disables sounding received beacons in CW
Controls > Cw > Enable	enables sounding received beacons in CW [off]
Controls > Cw > Set_speed	select words-per-minute of CW soundings [15]
Controls > Cw > Test	test CW sounding function
Controls > Dr	turn on/off dead reckoning [off]
Controls > Filters > Fade	turn on/off filtering currently inactive stations [on]
Controls > Filters > Hf_gateway	turn on/off filtering of stations gatewayed from HF [off]
Controls > Filters > Junk	turn on/off filtering data embedded with control characters [off]
Controls > Filters > Limit	turn on/off filtering of long Unprotocol paths [off]
Controls > Filters > Other_beacons	turn on/off filtering non-beacon packets [on]
Controls > Filters > Pos_filter	turn on/off filtering of random GPS data errors [on]
Controls > Log	turn on/off automatic logging of track histories [off]
Controls > Metric	select map measurements in kilometers or miles [miles]

Controls > Uplinks	turn on/off transmitting your object data [on]
Controls > Xmt	turn on/off normal transmitting [off]
Digis	display digipeaters used by all received stations
Erase	delete outgoing message
Files > Append	load a backup file without losing current station data
Files > Dos	transfer to DOS
Files > Ethernet	periodically save Backup file to storage device on Ethernet LAN
Files > Get	connect via telephone line modem to receive worldwide APRS activity
Files > Hang-up	hang-up phone manually when connected to a modem
Files > Load	load a backup file
Files > New	create a new file
Files > Print	print selected file
Files > Replay	load and play saved track history files
Files > Save	save current data
Files > sOrt	sort station list in chronological order with oldest stations first
Goto	move cursor to your station or tracked station
Heard	display packets per hour received from each station during previous 24 hours
Inputs > Add_object	add an object to the APRS map at the current cursor position
Inputs > Df	enter a beam heading or signal report for direction finding
Inputs > My > Bulletin_group	enter the bulletin group for your station
Inputs > My > Heading	enter the direction of your vehicle
Inputs > My > Message_group	enter the message group for your station

Inputs > My > Posit	enter the position of your station
Inputs > My > Radar	configure proximity sensor for your station
Inputs > My > Status	enter the status text for your station
Inputs > Pwr_ht_gain	enter the transmitter power and antenna parameters of your station
Inputs > Resources	enter resource information
Inputs > Save_pos	save the current position of your station as an object
Inputs > Up_pos	save the current position of your station as an object
Just > All	clear map and display all stations
Just > Digipeaters	clear map and display only digipeaters
Just > Icons	clear map and display only station icons
Just > Mobiles	clear map and display only moving stations
Just > Non_qth	clear map and display all stations that are not QTHs
Just > oBjects	clear map and display only objects
Just > One	clear map and display only one station type
Just > Print	print a selected subset of objects to the printer
Just > Special	clear map and display only stations using special symbols
Just > Wx	clear map and display only weather stations
Kill	delete incoming message
List > Dx	display list of latest received DX spots
List > Log	display list of latest received status, message, and telemetry packets
List > Resources	display list of other local APRS assets
List > Status	display list of latest received status packets
List > Telemetry	display list of latest received telemetry packets
Maps > Config > Background	change map background color
Maps > Config > Change_map_list	change current MAPLIST.XXX file

Maps > Config > List_map_list	display list of all available MAPLIST.XXX files
Maps > Config > Offset_datum	offset map to match known GPS position
Maps > Distros	display list of all loaded maps
Maps > Down	magnify map
Maps > Features > *railroad	turn on/off display of railroads on map [on]
Maps > Features > All	turn on/off display of all map features [on]
Maps > Features > Borders	turn on/off display of map borders [on]
Maps > Features > Calls	turn on/off display of call signs on map [on]
Maps > Features > Dim	turn on/off dimmed map display [off]
Maps > Features > Headings	turn on/off display of headings on map [on]
Maps > Features > Labels	turn on/off display of labels on map [on]
Maps > Features > Roads	turn on/off display of roads on map [on]
Maps > Features > Water	turn on/off display of waterways on map [on]
Maps > Hierarchy	display hierarchy of available maps
Maps > Lock	lock currently displayed map to override automatic map selection function
Maps > Mile_markers	locate mile marker on a U.S. Interstate highway (except California)
Maps > Overlays > Atv	display Amateur Television (ATV) overlay on map
Maps > Overlays > Crash	display crash overlay on map
Maps > Overlays > Digipeaters	display digipeater overlay on map
Maps > Overlays > Frequencies	display APRS frequency overlay on map
Maps > Overlays > Gates	display gateway overlay on map
Maps > Overlays > National_weather_service	display NWS station overlay on map

Maps > Overlays > Other	display other overlays on map
Maps > Overlays > Radio Shack	display Radio Shack overlay on map
Maps > Overlays > Stores	display ham radio store overlay on map
Maps > Overlays > Zips	display ZIP Code overlay on map
Maps > Plots > Borders	display perimeters of all selectable maps
Maps > Plots > Cap_grids	overlay Civil Air Patrol (CAP) grid squares on map
Maps > Plots > compressed_Format	display compressed formats in ASCII
Maps > Plots > Df	display coverage circles representing reported signal strengths of unknown source
Maps > Plots > Grid_square	overlay 2-character Maidenhead grid squares on map
Maps > Plots > Pwr_ht_gain	display circles representing station coverage area
Maps > Plots > Range_rings	display coverage circles at 1, 3/4, 1/2, and 1/4 of the coverage circle scale
Maps > Plots > Traffic	displays lines between stations exchanging messages
Maps > Save	save current map
Maps > Show > Alt	display map, if any, under currently displayed map
Maps > Show > Callsigns	display call signs
Maps > Show > Map_overlays	display map overlays
Maps > Up	reduce map
Next	move cursor to next weather station and display its weather data
Operations > Alarms_clear	clear your alarms
Operations > Communications	disable APRS and open window for direct communications with device connected to serial port
Operations > Digipath	configure alternative Unprotocol paths

Operations > Find	locate a call sign or grid square
Operations > Replay_tracks	play a track history
Operations > Unprotocol	configure your primary Unprotocol path
Positions	display received APRS position packets
Quit	quit APRS (DOS)
Read	display transmitted and received messages
Send	compose and transmit message or bulletin
Traffic	display last 23 lines of received traffic
Unproto	configure the normal digipeater path for your station
View	display scrolling list of all received packets
Weather > Alarms > Clear_alarm	clear weather alarms
Weather > Alarms > High_temp	configure high temperature alarm
Weather > Alarms > Low_temp	configure low temperature alarm
Weather > Alarms > Rain	configure rain alarm
Weather > Alarms > rAnge	limit weather alarms from stations within a selectable distance
Weather > Alarms > Wind	configure wind alarm
Weather > Alarms > Zero_rain	set the rain gauge measurement to 0
Weather > Callsign_format > Baro	display atmospheric pressure and time of report
Weather > Callsign_format > Callsigns	display call signs of weather stations
Weather > Callsign_format > None	clear weather data display
Weather > Callsign_format > Other_symbols	turn on/off alternate weather symbols [off]
Weather > Callsign_format > Spd/alt	display wind speed
Weather > Callsign_format > Temps	display temperature and rainfall reading
Weather > Callsign_format > Winds	display wind speed and rainfall readings and time of report.

Weather > Displays > Just_wx	limit map display to weather stations
Weather > Displays > No_counties	do not display county weather alarms
Weather > Displays > Show_counties	display county weather alarms
Weather > Displays > Temps	display temperature data
Weather > Displays > Winds	display wind data
Weather > Enter	manually input a weather report
Weather > Log	saves received weather data in the track history file
Weather > Metric	use metric system for weather station data
Weather > Query	transmit an APRS weather station query packet
Xmt > All	transmit all your outstanding packets
Xmt > Bulletins	transmit all your outstanding bulletin packets
Xmt > Cq	transmit a CQ packet
Xmt > Last_ack	transmit a message acknowledgment
Xmt > Messages	transmit all your outstanding message packets
Xmt > Objects	transmit all your outstanding objects packets
Xmt > Posits	transmit all your outstanding position packets
Xmt > Query	transmit an APRS query packet
Xmt > Resource	transmit a resource information packet
Xmt > Status.	transmit all your outstanding status packets
Y axis	turn on/off 3-dimensional display of currently selected map [off]

APRS+SA

You choose most APRS+SA commands by selecting a command from a pull-down menu or pull-down sub-menu, for example, to enter the File > Start Logging TNC Data command, pull down the File menu and select Start Logging TNC Data. A few APRS+SA commands are selected by typing a control-character (e.g., [Home]).

When you open a tab in APRS+SA, you select commands for that tab from a pop-up menu. To view the pop-up menu, move the mouse cursor over the applicable tab window and press the right mouse button. (The commands for each tab are listed after the APRS+SA menu commands.)

Some APRS+SA commands have keyboard shortcuts, which are listed in brackets (e.g., [Ctrl-C]) in the Menu Command column. You enter these shortcuts by holding down the Control [Ctrl] key and pressing a second key, for example, to use the [Ctrl-C] shortcut, you press the C key, while holding down the Ctrl key.

Menu Command [Keyboard Shortcut]

Menu Command [Keyboard Shortcut]	Description
File > Open SA4/SA5/MN3 Overlay file	display Street Atlas overlay file on map
File > Clear Overlay file	remove Street Atlas overlay file from map
File > POS File to Map	display data from position log file on map
File > Open Position Log File	start saving position data to a file
File > Start Logging TNC Data	start saving TNC data to a file
File > Start Logging Internet Data	start saving Internet data to a file
File > Open Text Log File	load log file saved in text format
File > APRS+Text Editor	open text editor
File > Load Patch Files	load APRS+SA software patches
File > Exit	quit APRS+SA
Edit > Cut [Ctrl-X]	delete selected item and duplicate to clipboard
Edit > Copy [Ctrl-C]	duplicate selected item to clipboard

Edit > Paste [Ctrl-V]	insert item contained in clipboard
Edit > Find	locate item
Edit > Popup	display popup menu
View > Status Bar	turn on/off display of status bar
View > Tooltips	turn on/off display of tooltips
Setup	displays Setup window
Log	displays Event Log
Send > Send Message [Ctrl-M]	compose and transmit a message
Send > Transmit Position [Ctrl-P]	send position packet
Send > Transmit Station [Ctrl-S]	send status packet
Send > Send Bulletin [Ctrl-B]	compose and transmit a bulletin
Send > Send Weather Report [Ctrl-W]	compose and transmit a weather message
Send > Send Tactical Callsign	transmit tactical call sign
Object > Create Object from Map	create object located at lower left corner of map
Object > Create Object Manually	create object
Object > Create Object at My Current Location	create object located at current location of your station
Commands > Scrolling On/Off [Ctrl-Shift-P]	turn on/off map scrolling
Commands > Unproto Paths [Ctrl-Shift-U]	configure Unprotocol path(s) for your station
Commands > Map Features [Ctrl-Shift-M]	select map display options
Commands > Start Street Atlas [Ctrl-Shift-A]	begin running Street Atlas
Commands > Coordinate Convention [Ctrl-Shift-C]	display Coordinate Conversion window
Commands > TNC Commands > TNC Port 1 [Ctrl-Shift-1]	select TNC on serial port 1
Commands > TNC Commands > TNC Port 2 [Ctrl-Shift-2]	select TNC on serial port 2
Commands > TNC Commands > Send [Ctrl-C To TNC] [Ctrl-C]	transmit control character Ctrl-C to TNC

Commands > TNC Commands > Send Three [Ctrl-Cs To TNC [Ctrl-R]	transmit three control character Ctrl-Cs to TNC
Commands > TNC Commands > Pico Position Text [Ctrl-E]	transmit position packet to PacComm Pico TNC
Commands > TNC Commands > Garmin Handheld Receivers	display Garmin GRMN/GRMN Interface window
Commands > TNC Commands > Tripmate > ASTRAL To TNC Port	use TNC port for Tripmate GPS communications
Commands > TNC Commands > Tripmate > ASTRAL To GPS Port	use GPS port for Tripmate GPS communications
Commands > TNC Commands > Flow Control Debugging - HSP	display Flow Control Debug window
Commands > ?APRS? [Ctrl-Q]	send APRS query packet
Commands > Time Filter > Off	process all data despite its age
Commands > Time Filter > 0.5, 1, 2, 3, 4, 8, 12, 24 Hours	ignore data older than selected time period
Commands > Range Filter > Off	process data from all stations despite their
Commands > Range Filter > 3, 5, 10, 20, 40, 80, 160, 320, 640, 1280, 2560 Miles	ignore data from stations beyond selected distance from your station
distance from your station	
Commands > Maps > Map Drawing On [Ctrl+=]	turn on map drawing
Commands > Maps > Map Drawing Off [Ctrl+-]	turn off map drawing
Commands > Maps > Locate Yourself On The Map [Ctrl-L]	display position of your station on map
Commands > Maps > Draw Map 1 through 9 [Ctrl-1 through Ctrl-9]	display selected map
Commands > Maps > Draw Next Map 0 [Ctrl-0]	display next map in Map tab list
Commands > Summary Window	display Summary window
Commands > Calculator [Ctrl-Alt-Shift-A]	display calculator

Commands > Clear > Clear All	remove contents of all windows
Commands > Clear > Clear Position Data	remove position data from all windows
Commands > Clear > Keep Most Recent	remove contents of all windows except the most recent data
Commands > Clear > Keep Station Within Range	remove contents of all windows except data related to stations within range of your station
Commands > Clear > Remove Lat/Long 0 90 180	remove data related to stations with latitudes or longitudes of 0, 90, and 180 degrees
Commands > Clear > Clear TNC Window	remove contents of TNC window
Commands > Clear > Clear TCP/IP Window	remove contents of TCP/IP window
Commands > Clear > Clear GPS Window	remove contents of GPS window
Commands > Speak Last Status Text [Ctrl-Shift-T]	convert text in last received status packet to speech
Commands > Internet Connect	connect to APRServer
Commands > Callsign Lookup on the Internet	connect to call sign server via the Internet
Speech > Enable	turn on text-to-speech function
Speech > Disable	turn off text-to-speech function
Speech > Stop	turn off text-to-speech function
Speech > Sound Effects On	enable sound effects
Speech > Sound Effects Off	disable sound effects
Bitmap	display map of North America
About	display information concerning APRS+SA
Positions Tab Popup Menu	Description
Locate > Current Position	display location of selected station on map
Locate > Stations in Range	display location (on map) of stations within range of selected station

Locate > Nearest Station To	display location (on map) of station nearest to selected station
Lists > Add to Keep Recent Only List	append selected station to Keep Recent Only List
Lists > Add to Ignore List	append selected station to Ignore List
Coordinates	copy coordinates of selected station in Coordinate Conversion window
Keep Most Recent Position Only	retain only the newest position data of selected station
Delete Station	remove selected station
Archive Position Data to Disk	save position data of selected station to disk
Add to Tracking List	add selected station to Tracking List
Show in History Tab	display selected station to History tab list
Make Location Map Center	redraw map centered on location of selected station
Filter Location Data	remove location of selected station from map
Send Message To	compose and transmit message to selected station
Upload to Garmin GPS	transfer position data of selected station to Garmin GPS receiver
Clear Selection	deselect selected station
Range to Station	display distance to selected station from your station
?APRS?	send APRS query packet to selected station
Sort by Range	display stations in list arranged according to distance from your station
View > Report Mode	display station data as a report
View > List Mode	display station data as a list
View > Adjust Column Width	change the width of the displayed columns for best viewing
Print	print window contents
Clipboard > Copy Rows to Clipboad	duplicate selected rows to clipboard
Clipboard > Copy Callsign to Clipboard	duplicate call sign field of selected row to clipboard
Clipboard > Copy Text to Clipboard	duplicate text field of selected row to clipboard

Track Tab Popup Menu

	Description
Locate > Current Position	display location of selected station on map
Locate > Stations in Range	display location (on map) of stations within range of selected station
Locate > Nearest Station To	display location (on map) of station nearest to selected station
Lists > Add to Keep Recent Only List	append selected station to Keep Recent Only List
Lists > Add to Ignore List	append selected station to Ignore List
Coordinates	copy coordinates of selected station in Coordinate Conversion window
Keep Most Recent Position Only	retain only the newest position data of selected station
Delete Station	remove selected station
Archive Position Data to Disk	save position data of selected station to disk
Add to Tracking List	add selected station to Tracking List
Show in History Tab	display selected station to History tab list
Make Location Map Center	redraw map centered on location of selected station
Filter Location Data	remove location of selected station from map
Send Message To	compose and transmit message to selected station
Upload to Garmin GPS	transfer position data of selected station to Garmin GPS receiver
Clear Selection	deselect selected station
Range to Station	display distance to selected station from your station
?APRS?	send APRS query packet to selected station
Sort by Range	display stations in list arranged according to distance from your station
View > Report Mode	display station data as a report
View > List Mode	display station data as a list
View > Adjust Column Width	change the width of the displayed columns for best viewing

Print — print window contents
Clipboard > Copy Rows to Clipboard — duplicate selected rows to clipboard
Clipboard > Copy Callsign to Clipboard — duplicate call sign field of selected row to clipboard
Clipboard > Copy Text to Clipboard — duplicate selected text to clipboard

History Tab Popup Menu

Description

Locate Position — display location of selected station on map
Locate Stations in Range — display location (on map) of stations within range of selected station
Locate Nearest Station To — display location (on map) of station nearest to selected station
Range — display distance and compass direction to selected station
Coordinates — copy coordinates of selected station in Coordinate Conversion window
Delete Position Fix — remove selected position packet from window
Send Message To — compose and transmit message to selected station
Upload to Garmin GPS — transfer position data of selected station to Garmin GPS receiver
Add to Tracking List — add selected station to Tracking List
Lists > Add to Keep Recent Only List — append selected station to Keep Recent Only List
Lists > Add to Ignore List — append selected station to Ignore List
Filter Position Reports — remove position packets according to packet filtering criteria
Adjust Column Width — change the width of the displayed columns for best viewing
Print — print window contents
Copy Rows to Clipboard — duplicate selected rows to clipboard

Maps Tab Popup Menu

Description

Clear List — remove contents of list

Delete	remove selected item from list
Maps > Map 1: Map 1 through Map 9: Map 9	add Map 1: Map 1 through Map 9: Map 9 to list
Weather > Temperature	add Temperature to list
Weather > Baro. Pressure	add Baro. Pressure to list
Weather > Wind Speed	add Wind Speed to list
Weather > Wind Direction	add Wind Direction to list
Weather > Winds	add Winds to list
Weather > Humidity	add Humidity to list
Maps by Icon > Digipeaters	add Digipeaters to list
Maps by Icon > By Icon 1 through By Icon 4	add By Icon 1 through By Icon 4 to list
Other Maps > History Page Map	add History Page to list
Other Maps > Posit Text Search	add Posit Text to list
Other Maps > Status Text Search	add Status Text to list
Other Maps > Fixed Stations	add Fixed Stations to list
Other Maps > Moving Stations	add Moving Stations to list
Other Maps > HF Gated Stations	add HF Gated Stations to list
Other Maps > APRS+SA Stations	add APRS+SA Stations to list
Custom Scripted > Create Custom Script	create custom map
Custom Scripted > (list of custom maps)	add custom map to list

Status Tab Popup Menu

	Description
Delete Message(s)	
Send Message To	compose and transmit message to selected station
Clear Page	remove contents of window

Locate on Map	display location of selected station on map
Locate Stations in Range	display location (on map) of stations within range of selected station
Locate Nearest Station To	display location (on map) of station nearest to selected station
Range to Station	display distance to selected station from your station
Sort by Range	display stations in list arranged according to distance from your station
Sort by Icon	display stations in list arranged according to icon
Show History	display all the packets received from selected station
Adjust Column Width	change the width of the displayed columns for best viewing
Print	print window contents
Clipboard > Copy to Clipboad	duplicate selected item to clipboard
Clipboard > Copy Text to Clipboard	duplicate text field of selected row to clipboard
Clipboard > Copy Callsign to Clipboard	duplicate call sign field of selected row to clipboard

Traffic Tab Popup Menu | **Description**
Delete Message(s)	remove selected message(s)
Delete Messages From/To	remove messages from/to station originating selected message
Send Message To	compose and transmit message to station originating selected message
Clear Page	remove contents of window
Locate on Map	display location of station originating selected message
Locate Stations in Range	display location (on map) of stations within range of station originating selected message
Locate Nearest Station To	display location (on map) of station nearest to station originating selected message
Show History	display all the packets received from station originating selected message

Range to Station	display distance between your station and the station originating selected message
Range Between Stations	display distance between originating and receiving station of selected message
Remove Ack's	delete acknowledgement packets from history of listed stations
Adjust Column Width	change the width of the displayed columns for best viewing
Print	print window contents
Clipboard > Copy to Clipboad	duplicate selected item to clipboard
Clipboard > Copy Text to Clipboard	duplicate text of selected message to clipboard
Clipboard > Copy From Callsign to Clipboard	duplicate call sign of station originating selected message to clipboard
Clipboard > Copy To Callsign to Clipboard	duplicate call sign of station receiving selected message to clipboard

Messages Tab Popup Menu
(Window for Messages To/From Your Station)

	Description
Delete	remove selected message
Delete Ack'ed	remove acknowledged messages
Reset Interval	change interval field to 7.5
Transmit Now	send selected message immediately
Copy Message	duplicate contents of selected message in message composition window
Clear Page	remove contents of window
Clear Bulletins	remove bulletins from window
Clear Messages	remove messages from window
Path > I = Internet TCP/IP Port TCP	send message via Internet
Path > 1 = RELAY,WIDE Port 1	send message via Unprotocol path 1

Path > 2 = RELAY,WIDE Port 1	send message via Unprotocol path 1
Path > 3 = RELAY,WIDE Port 1	send message via Unprotocol path 1
Path > 4 = RELAY,WIDE Port 1	send message via Unprotocol path 1
Path > N = RELAY,WIDE Port 1	send message via Unprotocol path N
Path > S = RELAY,WIDE Port 1	send message via Unprotocol path S
Path > E = RELAY,WIDE Port 1	send message via Unprotocol path E
Path > W = RELAY,WIDE Port 1	send message via Unprotocol path W
Path > ECHO = ECHO Port 1	send message via Unprotocol path ECHO
Path > EG = ECHO,GATE Port 1	send message via Unprotocol path EG
Path > WIDE = WIDE Port 1	send message via Unprotocol path WIDE
Path > WW = WIDE,WIDE Port 1	send message via Unprotocol path WW
Path > = Default	send message via default Unprotocol path
Stop Transmission	cease sending selected message
Suspend Transmission	postpone sending selected message
Resume Transmission	continue sending selected message
Manual Acknowledge	set selected message manually
Adjust Column Width	change the width of the displayed columns for best viewing
Clipboard > Copy Text and Run	duplicate text of selected message to clipboard
Clipboard > Copy Callsign to Clipboard	duplicate call sign of station receiving selected message to clipboard
Clipboard > Copy Text to Clipboard	duplicate text of selected message to clipboard

Messages Tab Popup Menu
(Window for All Messages)

	Description
Delete Message(s)	remove selected message(s)
Send Message To	compose and transmit message to station originating selected message
Time Entered	display time selected message was entered
Copy Message	duplicate contents of selected message in message composition window
Sort by Callsign/Message Number	arrange messages in window by call sign and message number
Clear Page	remove contents of window
Locate on Map	display location (on map) of station originating selected message
Locate Stations in Range	display location (on map) of stations within range of station originating selected message
Locate Nearest Station To	display location (on map) of station nearest to station originating selected message
Range to Station	display distance from your station to station originating selected message
Show History	display all the packets received from station originating selected message
Adjust Column Width	change the width of the displayed columns for best viewing
Print	print window contents
Clipboard > Copy Text and Run	duplicate text of selected message to clipboard
Clipboard > Copy to Clipboad	duplicate selected item to clipboard
Clipboard > Copy Text to Clipboard	duplicate text of selected message to clipboard
Clipboard > Copy Callsign to Clipboard	duplicate call sign of station originating selected message to clipboard

Bulletins Tab Popup Menu

	Description
Delete Message(s)	remove selected bulletin(s)
Delete Messages From/To	remove bulletins from/to station originating selected bulletin
Send Message To	compose and transmit message to station originating selected bulletin
Time Entered	display time selected bulletin was entered
Clear Page	remove contents of window
Locate on Map	display location (on map) of station originating selected bulletin
Locate Stations in Range	display location (on map) of stations within range of station originating selected bulletin
Locate Nearest Station To	display location (on map) of station nearest to station originating selected bulletin
Adjust Column Width	change the width of the displayed columns for best viewing
Print	print window contents
Clipboard > Copy Text and Run	duplicate text of selected message to clipboard
Clipboard > Copy to Clipboad	duplicate selected item to clipboard
Clipboard > Copy Text to Clipboard	duplicate text of selected bulletin to clipboard
Clipboard > Copy To Callsign to Clipboard	duplicate call sign of station originating selected bulletin to clipboard

Objects Tab Popup Menu
(Window for Your Station's Objects)

	Description
Transmit Now	send selected object packet immediately
State > Active	resume sending packets for selected object
State > Kill	cease sending packets for selected object
State > Inactive	suspend sending packets for selected object
State > Persistent	set state of selected object to persistent

Transmit Interval > Every 5, 10, 15, 20, 30, 60 Minutes, 2, 3, 4, 6, 12 Hours	select how often packets for selected object are sent
Edit Object	change characteristics of selected object
Delete Object(s)	remove selected object
Create Object > Create Object from Map	create object located at lower left corner of map
Create Object > Create Object Manually	create object
Create Object > Create Object at My Current Location	create object located at current location of your station
Read SA Object File	load Street Atlas object file into APRS+SA
Clear Page	remove contents of window
Locate on Map	display location of selected object on map
Locate Stations in Range	display location (on map) of stations within range of selected object
Locate Nearest Station To	display location (on map) nearest station to selected object
Range to Object	display distance to selected object from your station
Adjust Column Width	change the width of the displayed columns for best viewing
Print	print window contents
Copy to Clipboard	duplicate selected item to clipboard

Objects Tab Popup Menu (Window for All Objects) **Description**

Locate > Current Position	display location of selected object on map
Locate > Stations in Range	display location (on map) of stations within range of selected object
Locate > Nearest Station To	display location (on map) of station nearest to selected object
Lists > Add to Keep Recent Only List	append selected object to Keep Recent Only List

Lists > Add to Ignore List	append selected object to Ignore List
Coordinates	copy coordinates of selected object in Coordinate Conversion window
Keep Most Recent Position Only	retain only the newest position data of selected object
Delete Station	remove selected object
Archive Position Data to Disk	save position data of selected object to disk
Add to Tracking List	add selected object to Tracking List
Show in History Tab	display selected object to History tab list
Make Location Map Center	redraw map centered on location of selected object
Filter Location Data	remove location of selected object from map
Send Message To	compose and transmit message to station originating selected object
Upload to Garmin GPS	transfer position data of selected object to Garmin GPS receiver
Clear Selection	deselect selected object
Range to Station	display distance to selected object from your station
?APRS?	send APRS query packet to selected object
Sort by Range	display objects in list arranged according to distance from your station
View > Report Mode	display objects data as a report
View > List Mode	display objects data as a list
View > Adjust Column Width	change the width of the displayed columns for best viewing
Print	print window contents
Clipboard > Copy Rows to Clipboard	duplicate selected rows to clipboard
Clipboard > Copy Callsign to Clipboard	duplicate call sign field of selected row to clipboard
Clipboard > Copy Text to Clipboard	duplicate text field of selected row to clipboard

Weather Tab Popup Menu

	Description
Delete Message(s)	remove selected message(s)
Send Message To	compose and transmit message to selected station
Clear Page	remove contents of window
Map > Temperature	display temperature of selected message at station location on map
Map > Barometric Pressure	display barometric pressure of selected message at station location on map
Map > Winds	display wind speed of selected message at station location on map
Locate on Map	display location of selected station on map
Locate Stations in Range	display location (on map) of stations within range of selected station
Locate Nearest Station To	display location (on map) of station nearest to selected station
Range to Station	display distance to selected station from your station
Sort by Range	display stations in list arranged according to distance from your station
Show History	display all the packets received from selected station
Adjust Column Width	change the width of the displayed columns for best viewing
Print	print window contents
Copy to Clipboad	duplicate selected item to clipboard

Telemetry Tab Popup Menu

	Description
Delete Observation(s)	remove selected telemetry
Send Message To	compose and transmit message to selected station
Clear Page	remove contents of window
Adjust Column Width	change the width of the displayed columns for best viewing
Print	print window contents
Copy to Clipboad	duplicate selected item to clipboard

TNC Tab Popup Menu

	Description
Undo	cancel previous action
Cut	delete selected item and duplicate to clipboard
Copy	duplicate selected item to clipboard
Paste	insert item contained in clipboard
Delete	remove selected item
Select All	choose all items

GPS Tab Popup Menu

	Description
Undo	cancel previous action
Cut	delete selected item and duplicate to clipboard
Copy	duplicate selected item to clipboard
Paste	insert item contained in clipboard
Delete	remove selected item
Select All	choose all items

TCP Tab Popup Menu

	Description
Undo	cancel previous action
Cut	delete selected item and duplicate to clipboard
Copy	duplicate selected item to clipboard
Paste	insert item contained in clipboard
Delete	remove selected item
Select All	choose all items

MacAPRS

You enter most MacAPRS commands by selecting a command from a pull-down menu or pull-down sub-menu, for example, to select the Edit - Clear Stations and Messages command, pull down the Edit menu and select Clear Stations and Messages. A few MacAPRS commands are selected by typing a control-character (e.g., [Home]).

Some MacAPRS commands have keyboard shortcuts, which are listed in brackets (e.g., [Cmd-O]) in the Menu Command column. You enter the shortcuts by holding down the Command [Cmd] key and pressing a second key, for example, to use the [Cmd-O] shortcut, you press the O key, while holding down the Cmd key.

Menu Command [Keyboard Shortcut]	Description
Apple > About MacAPRS	display information concerning MacAPRS
Apple > Bug Report	display form for reporting MacAPRS problems
File > New...	open new map window with default map
File > Open File... [Cmd-O]	load saved file into MacAPRS
File > Open Call Sign File...	load call sign directory file into MacAPRS
File > Close Window [Cmd-W]	close active open window
File > Save... [Cmd-S]	save displayed information as a file
File > Auto Save Map Window Image...	turn on/off automatic saving of active map
File > Save Window as HTML...	save displayed information in HTML format
File > Save Window Configuration...	create file containing current settings of windows
File > Simulate...	load file to simulate APRS activity
File > Get Map Info [Cmd-I]	display information regarding active map
File > Page Setup...	select printing parameters
File > Print... [Cmd-P]	print active open window
File > Merge Map Files...	combine maps to create new map

File > Quit [Cmd-Q]	quit MacAPRS
Edit > Cut [Cmd-X]	delete selected item and duplicate to clipboard
Edit > Copy [Cmd-C]	duplicate selected item to clipboard
Edit > Paste [Ctrl-V]	insert item contained in clipboard
Edit > Clear	delete selected item
Edit > Select All [Cmd-A]	choose all items in list
Edit > Find... [Cmd-F]	find station on map
Edit > Find Again... [Cmd-G]	repeat previous Edit > Find command
Edit > Calculate Distances... [Cmd-=]	determine distance and antenna bearing between received stations
Edit > Edit/Add Station/Object... [Cmd-E]	add or change station or object on map
Edit > Edit/Add Weather/Object...	add or change weather object on map
Edit > Edit/Add Waypoint...	add or change waypoint on map
Edit > Clear Stations	delete received station information
Edit > Clear Messages	delete received messages
Edit > Clear Wind Data	delete received wind data
Edit > Clear Region Search Index	delete contents of region search index
Settings > Master Mode > Normal Ham Operation	configure MacAPRS for normal APRS operation
Settings > Master Mode > Weather ONLY	configure MacAPRS for NWS/SKYWARN weather station operation
Settings > Master Mode > Space Mode	configure MacAPRS for MIR space station operation
Settings > Master Mode > Radio Dir Finding Extras	configure MacAPRS with additional direction finding features
Settings > General Display Settings...	configure miscellaneous map display options
Settings > Station Settings....	configure MacAPRS with station parameters

Settings > Select TNC Type...	choose type of TNC used with MacAPRS
Settings > TNC Settings...	configure MacAPRS with TNC parameters
Settings > Position Report Rate Settings...	configure rate of position packet transmissions
Settings > GPS Settings...	configure
Settings > MacAPRS Settings...	configure MacAPRS with APRS parameters
Settings > DataBase Settings...	configure CD-ROM call sign directory
Settings > Weather Settings...	configure MacAPRS with weather station equipment parameters
Settings > Sound Settings...	configure MacAPRS sound options
Settings > Balloon Settings...	configure balloon tracking options
Settings > KISS Mode Settings...	configure options for KISS mode
Settings > Communications... > HF (or Dual Port) TNC	configure serial port for HF TNC
Settings > Communications... > VHF TNC	configure serial port for VHF/UHF TNC
Settings > Communications... > NMEA/GPS	configure serial port for NMEA/GPS equipment
Settings > Communications... > Weather	configure serial port for weather station equipment
Settings > Communications... > Direction Finding	configure serial port for direction finding equipment
Settings > Communications... > Radio Control	configure serial port for radio control
Settings > Communications... > not used	not used
Settings > Communications... > Binary Input	configure serial port for binary input
Settings > Communications... > Echo Port	configure serial port as an echo port
Settings > TNC Commands > Send Position [Cmd-T]	transmit position packet
Settings > TNC Commands > Send Objects	transmit objects packet
Settings > TNC Commands > Send Grid-Square Position [Cmd-.]	transmit Maidenhead grid square packet
Settings > TNC Commands > Send Weather Report	transmit weather report packet

Settings > TNC Commands > Send RDF Report	transmit direction finding packet
Settings > TNC Commands > Send APRS Query [Cmd-/]	transmit APRS station query packet
Settings > TNC Commands > Send WX Query	transmit an APRS weather station query packet
Settings > TNC Commands > Send IGate Query	transmit APRS IGate station query packet
Settings > TNC Commands > VHF-Reinitialize TNC parameters	configure VHF/UHF TNC with TNC Settings
Settings > TNC Commands > VHF-Exit KISS Mode	force VHF/UHF TNC to quit KISS mode
Settings > TNC Commands > VHF-Exit Kantronics Host Mode mode	force VHF/UHF TNC to quit Kantronics TNC host
Settings > TNC Commands > VHF-Exit AEA Host Mode	force VHF/UHF TNC to quit AEA TNC host mode
Settings > TNC Commands > HF-Reinitialize TNC	configure HF TNC with TNC Settings parameters
Settings > TNC Commands > HF-Exit KISS Mode	force HF TNC to quit KISS mode
Settings > TNC Commands > HF-Exit Kantronics Host Mode	force HF TNC to quit Kantronics TNC host mode
Settings > TNC Commands > HF-Exit AEA Host Mode	force HF TNC to quit AEA TNC host mode
Settings > Terminal Settings	configure settings for direct communications with TNC
Settings > Unproto APRSM Via (HF or Dual Port) > -None-	configure no Unproto HF path
Settings > Unproto APRSM Via (HF or Dual Port) > Default	configure Unproto HF path with default path
Settings > Unproto APRSM Via (HF or Dual Port) > Other...	configure Unproto HF path with user-defined path
Settings > Unproto APRSM Via (HF or Dual Port) > relay,WIDE	configure Unproto HF path as RELAY,WIDE
Settings > Unproto APRSM Via (HF or Dual Port) > WIDE,WIDE	configure Unproto HF path as WIDE,WIDE
Settings > Unproto APRSM Via (HF or Dual Port) > WIDE,GATE	configure Unproto HF path as WIDE,GATE
Settings > Unproto APRSM Via (HF or Dual Port) > WIDE-3	configure Unproto HF path as WIDE-3
Settings > Unproto APRSM Via (VHF) > -None-	configure no Unproto VHF/UHF path
Settings > Unproto APRSM Via (VHF) > Default	configure Unproto VHF/UHF path with default path

Settings > Unproto APRSM Via (VHF) > Other...	configure Unproto VHF/UHF path with user-defined path
Settings > Unproto APRSM Via (VHF) > relay,WIDE	configure Unproto VHF/UHF path as RELAY, WIDE
Settings > Unproto APRSM Via (VHF) > WIDE,WIDE	configure Unproto VHF/UHF path as WIDE,WIDE
Settings > Unproto APRSM Via (VHF) > WIDE,GATE	configure Unproto VHF/UHF path as WIDE,GATE
Settings > Unproto APRSM Via (VHF) > WIDE-3	configure Unproto VHF/UHF path as WIDE-3
Settings > Open HF TNC (Dual Port)	turn on/off communications with HF TNC
Settings > Open VHF TNC	turn on/off communications with VHF/UHF TNC
Settings > Open GPS/NMEA	turn on/off communications with NMEA/GPS equipment
Settings > Open Weather Station	turn on/off communications with weather station equipment
Settings > Open Direction Finding	turn on/off communications with direction finding equipment
Settings > Open Hard Copy Logging	turn on/off logging to printer
Settings > Open Echo Port	turn on/off echo port communications
Settings > Stop All Input	terminate all serial port communications
Settings > TCP/IP Connections > TCP/IP Settings	configure options regarding APRServer connections
Settings > TCP/IP Connections > Show TCP/IP Host List	display list of APRServers
Settings > TCP/IP Connections > Close All TCP ports	disconnect from all APRServer
Settings > TCP/IP Connections > Open Internet DGPS	connect to Differential GPS server
Settings > TCP/IP Connections > Connect To APRServe Network	connect to APRServer network
Settings > TCP/IP Connections > (server names)	connect to selected APRServer from list

Settings > Flag All Macs	log all stations using Macintosh OS to flagged station list
Settings > Flag All Windows	log all stations using Windows OS to flagged station list
Settings > GPS Alarm	configure options regarding GPS equipment alarms
Settings > Set Time from GPS	turn on/off determining MacAPRS time from GPS equipment
Settings > GPS Setup...	configure options regarding GPS equipment
Logging > Station Logging	turn on/off recording received station data
Logging > APRS Logging	turn on/off recording received APRS data
Logging > NMEA Logging	turn on/off recording received NMEA/GPS data
Logging > Local Weather Logging	turn on/off recording local weather reports
Logging > Message Logging	turn on/off recording received messages
Logging > Local RDF Logging	turn on/off recording local direction finding data
Logging > Statistics Logging	turn on/off recording received packet statistics
Logging > Stop All Logging	disable recording all received data
Maps > (map names)	display selected map from list
Display > Station Display Mode > Display All Stations	turn on/off display of all received stations on map
Display > Station Display Mode > Display Direct Stations Only	turn on/off display of directly received stations on map
Display > Station Display Mode > Display Flagged Stations Only	turn on/off display of only received flagged stations on map
Display > Station Display Mode > Display Tracked Stations Only	turn on/off display of only received tracked stations on map

Display > Station Display Mode > Display Weather Stations Only — turn on/off display of only received weather stations on map

Display > Station Display Mode > Station Display Mode... — configure options regarding display of stations on map

Display > Map Display Options — configure options regarding display of maps

Display > Home View (Home) [Cmd-H] — display current map in its default size

Display > Clear/Redraw [Cmd-L] — delete received data from map

Display > Center View — display center of map at mouse pointer location

Display > Zoom In 2X [Page Down] — magnify map by factor of 2

Display > Zoom In 4X — magnify map by factor of 4

Display > Zoom Out 2X [Page Up] — decrease map magnification by factor of 2

Display > Map Boundaries [Cmd-B] — display perimeters of available maps

Display > Overlays... > Display Overlay — display selected map overlay

Display > Overlays... > Display Overlay List — display list of map overlay components

Display > Overlays... > (overlay names) — select map overlay from list

Display > GridSquare (2 Ltr) — overlay 2-character Maidenhead grid squares on map

Display > GridSquare (4 Ltr) — overlay 4-character Maidenhead grid squares on map

Display > GridSquare (6 Ltr) — overlay 6-character Maidenhead grid squares on map

Display > Lat/Lon Lines — overlay latitude and longitude lines on map

Display > C.A.P. 15' Grids — overlay Civil Air Patrol grid squares on map

Display > Display Icons — turn on/off display of received station icons on map

Display > Display Call Signs — turn on/off display of received station call signs on map

Display > Display Labels — turn on/off display of labels on map

Display > Display Symbols — turn on/off display of symbols on map

Display > Display Filled Polygons — turn on/off display of filled polygons

Display > Display APRS Info (Bottom of Screen)   turn on/off display of most recently received APRS data at bottom of map

Display > Display NMEA Info (Bottom of Screen)   turn on/off display of most recently received NMEA data at bottom of map

Display > Display Course and Speed Vectors   turn on/off display of course and speed vectors of moving objects on map

Display > Display Dead Reckoning   turn on/off display of dead reckoning data

Display > Auto Scroll Moving Map   turn on/off automatic scrolling map function

Display > Display Airports   display location of airports on map

Display > Display Zip Codes   display location of ZIP Codes on map

Display > Display Coverage Circles [Cmd-D]   display circles representing received stations' coverage area

Display > Replay Selected Station [Cmd-R]   display course of selected tracked station on map

Display > Relay All Tracks   display course of all tracked station on map

Display > Display Balloon Prediction [Cmd-J]   display balloon prediction data

Display > Enable Deleted Stations   display previously deleted stations on map

Display > Delete Old Stations   delete old received stations from map

Lists > New Message... [Cmd-M]   compose and transmit new message or bulletin

Lists > Message List [Cmd-4]   display list of transmitted and received messages and bulletins

Lists > New NTS Message...   compose and transmit new National Traffic System message

Lists > NTS Message List   display list of transmitted and received National Traffic System messages

Lists > Map List	display list of available maps
Lists > Map Label List	display list of map labels
Lists > Station List [Cmd-1]	display list of received packet stations
Lists > Position List [Cmd-2]	display list of position information regarding received stations
Lists > When Heard	display list and graph of times that stations were received
Lists > Weather List [Cmd-3]	display list of received weather station data
Lists > Shelter List	display list of received emergency shelter object data
Lists > Hurricane List	display list of received hurricane object data
Lists > Flagged Station List	display list of received flagged stations
Lists > Track List	display list of received tracked station data
Lists > TCP/IP List	display list of data concerning stations received via the APRServer
Lists > Mic Enc List	display list of received MIC Encoder station data
Lists > RDF List	display list of received direction finding station data
Lists > ProtoPath List	display list of received stations' Unproto paths
Lists > History List [Cmd-5]	display list of all received packets
Lists > CallBook List [Cmd-0]	display list of CD-ROM call sign directory entries
Lists > APRS Statistics [Cmd-6]	display graphic representing APRS activity for previous day, week, year
Lists > Weather Display [Cmd-8]	display graphic representing local weather station equipment
Lists > 24 Hr Weather Charts [Cmd-7]	display graphic representing local weather data for previous 24 hours

Lists > NWS-Counties list	display list of counties with National Weather System alarms
Lists > NMEA Display [Cmd-9]	display GPS receiver heads up window
Lists > Altitude Statistics	display chart representing altitude statistics
Lists > Wind Interpolation	display graphic representing wind interpolation
Lists > Icon List	display list of MacAPRS icons
Lists > Global Label List	display list of global labels
Lists > Airport List	display list of airports
Lists > Internal State	display various MacAPRS parameters
Lists > Packet Statistics	display statistics regarding received packet activity
Lists > DX Countries List	display list of received DX stations
Lists > IOTA List	display list of received islands
Lists > Way Point List	display list of received waypoints
Lists > IGate Stations List	display list of received IGate stations
Windows > Next Window [Cmd-']	deselect active window and select an inactive window
Windows > New Map Window Square [Cmd-N]	open new map window with default map
Windows > New Map Window Polar	open new map window with default map in polar projection
Windows > New Map Window DEM	open new map window with selected Digital Elevation Model map
Windows > New Map Window DEM > About DEM	display help for Digital Elevation Model maps
Windows > New Map Window DEM > (map names)	display selected Digital Elevation Model map from list
Windows > New Map Window Tiger	display map received via Internet from Tiger server
Windows > New Map Window Intellicast > About Intellicast	display help for Intellicast weather maps

Windows > New Map Window Intellicast > Intellicast Composit	display composite weather map received via Internet from Intellicast
Windows > New Map Window Intellicast > (map names)	display selected weather map received via Internet from Intellicast server from list
Windows > Close All Windows	close all open windows
Windows > Stack All Windows	resize and arrange open windows in a
Windows > Tile Windows	resize and arrange open windows side-by-side
Windows > Reset Window Locations	resize and arrange open windows in a stack
Windows > Terminal Window	open window for direct communications with TNC
Windows > Garmin GPS Window	open window for controlling Garmin GPS receivers
Windows > ICONs	display all MacAPRS icons
Windows > TCP Connection Status	display information concerning connection to APRServer
Windows > (window names)	display selected map from list

pocketAPRS

You choose most pocketAPRS commands by tapping the Menu button, then selecting a command from a pull-down menu, for example, to select the Menu > Settings > Filters command, you tap the MENU button, tap the Settings menu and tap Filters. You choose immediate transmit commands by tapping the beach ball icon, then tapping the desired immediate transmit command. In the Map, Message, Station List, and Status List windows, you select a list command by tapping the down arrow (t), then tapping the desired list command.

Some pocketAPRS commands have shortcuts, which are listed in brackets (e.g., [/S]) in the Menu Command column. You enter the shortcuts in the Palm III Graffiti window by entering the command stroke and the applicable shortcut character, for example, to use the [/S] shortcut, enter the command stroke [/] and the letter S.

Menu Command [Keyboard Shortcut]	Description
Menu > Main > About pocketAPRS	display information concerning pocketAPRS
Menu > Main > pocketAPRS Help [/H]	display help for pocketAPRS
Menu > Main > Add Object [/A]	add, change, or delete an APRS object
Menu > Main > Send Message [/S]	compose and transmit message, bulletin, or announcement
Menu > Main > Manual DF Report [/D]	enter compass bearing for direction finding
Menu > Main > Edit Map List	delete map(s) from pocketAPRS
Menu > Main > Quit	quit pocketAPRS
Menu > Views > Map [/M]	display selected map
Menu > Views > Station List [/P]	display list of received stations
Menu > Views > Status List [/L]	display list of received station status information
Menu > Views > Messages [/M]	display list of received messages, bulletins, etc.
Menu > Views > View Packets [/V]	display list of received packets
Menu > Settings > pocketAPRS Settings	configure pocketAPRS parameters

Command	Description
Menu > Settings > Station Settings	configure station parameters
Menu > Settings > Filters	configure packet filtering
Menu > Settings > Transmit Control	configure packet transmission parameters
Menu > Settings > RDF Control	configure direction finding equipment parameters
Menu > Settings > Alarms & Alerts	configure APRS, digipeater, and GPS alerts and alarms
Menu > Settings > Map Display	configure map display options
Menu > Settings > Object Display	configure object display options
(Beach Ball Icon) > Transmit Position	send position packet
(Beach Ball Icon) > Transmit Status	send status packet
(Beach Ball Icon) > Transmit Objects	send APRS object packet
(Beach Ball Icon) > Transmit Messages	send message, bulletin, announcement, etc.
(Beach Ball Icon) > Transmit All	send all
(Beach Ball Icon) > APRS Query All	send APRS query packet
(Beach Ball Icon) > APRS Query Local	send APRS query packet to nearby stations
(Beach Ball Icon) > Reinitialize TNC	configure TNC with selected Settings menus parameters

Map Window Menu Command

Command	Description
t > 1/64 X to 64 X	increase/decrease map magnification by selected factor
(Map Icon) > (map names)	display selected map from list

Messages List Window Menu Command

Command	Description
t > All	display all messages and bulletins
t > Normal	display all messages only
t > Bulletins	display all bulletins only

t > Announcements   display all announcements only
t > Weather   display all weather messages only
t > Special Bulletins   display all special bulletins only

Station List/Status List Window Menu Command Description

t > Status	display list of status information regarding received stations
t > Position	display list of position information regarding received stations
t > Data	display list of station data regarding received stations
t > Distance	display list of distances between you and the received stations
t > Heard	display list of received stations in the order they were received
t > Digi Path	display list of Unprotocol path of received stations
t > Alerts	display list of alerts from received stations

TH-D7

You access menu selections in the Kenwood TH-D7 APRS Mode by pressing the MENU key, then either use the number keys to select the desired menu numbers or use the cursor keys to scroll to the desired menu number. Press the OK key to confirm a menu selection and press the MENU key to exit the menu mode.

Menu Command	Description
MENU-2-1	enter call sign and SSID
MENU-2-2	turn on/off operation with GPS receiver
MENU-2-3	enter station latitude and longitude
MENU-2-4	select MIC Encoder comment
MENU-2-5	select station icon
MENU-2-6	enter APRS status text

MENU-2-7   select beacon timing
MENU-2-8   enter Unprotocol path
MENU-2-9   select beacon transmission method
MENU-2-A   configure packet group code filtering
MENU-2-B   configure packet distance filtering
MENU-2-C   select units of measurement for distance and temperature

WinAPRS

You choose most Display > Direct Stations Only command, you pull down the Display menu and select Direct Stations Only. A few WinAPRS commands are entered by typing a control-character (e.g., [Home]), or pressing a function-key (e.g., [F5]).

Some WinAPRS commands have keyboard shortcuts which are listed in brackets (e.g., [B]) in the Menu Command column. You enter most WinAPRS shortcuts by simply typing the shortcut key, for example, to use the [B] shortcut, you type B.

Menu Command [Keyboard Shortcut]	Description
File > About WinAPRS	display information concerning WinAPRS
File > Open	load saved file into WinAPRS
File > Save [Ctrl-S]	save displayed information as a file
File > Save Window Config	create file containing current settings of windows
File > Close [Ctrl-W]	close active open window
File > Demo Mode	load file to demonstrate WinAPRS
File > Simulate...	load file to simulate APRS activity
File > Simulate Live GPS...	load file to simulate GPS activity

File > Print	print active open window
File > Exit	quit WinAPRS
Edit > Copy [Ctrl-C]	duplicate selected item to clipboard
Edit > Select All [Ctrl-A]	choose all items
Edit > Find [Ctrl-F]	find station on map
Edit > Find Again [Ctrl-G]	repeat previous Edit > Find command
Edit > Edit/Add Station/Object...	add or change station or object on map
Edit > Edit/Add Weather/Object...	add or change weather object on map
Edit > Clear Stations	delete received station information
Edit > Clear Messages	delete received messages
Settings > Master Mode > Normal Ham Operation	configure WinAPRS for normal APRS operation
Settings > Master Mode > Weather Only	configure WinAPRS for NWS/SKYWARN weather station operation
Settings > Master Mode > Space Mode	configure WinAPRS for MIR space station operation
Settings > Master Mode > Radio Dir Finding Extras	configure WinAPRS with additional direction finding features
Settings > General Display	configure miscellaneous map display options
Settings > Station	configure WinAPRS with station parameters
Settings > WinAPRS	configure WinAPRS with APRS parameters
Settings > Serial Port	configure serial port
Settings > Select TNC Type	choose type of TNC used with WinAPRS
Settings > TNC	configure WinAPRS with TNC parameters
Settings > Position Report Rate	configure rate of position packet transmissions
Settings > Weather	configure WinAPRS with weather station equipment parameters
Settings > CallBook DataBase	configure CD-ROM call sign directory

Command	Description
Settings > Enable Sound	configure WinAPRS sound options
Settings > Open VHF TNC	turn on/off communications with VHF/UHF TNC
Settings > Open HF TNC (Dual)	turn on/off communications with HF TNC
Settings > Open WX Port	turn on/off communications with weather station equipment
Settings > Open GPS Port	turn on/off communications with NMEA/GPS equipment
Settings > Open RDF Port	turn on/off communications with direction finding equipment
Settings > Close TNC	disable communications with TNC
Settings > Close All Ports	disable communications with all external equipment
Settings > KISS Mode Options	configure options for KISS mode
Settings > TNC Commands > Send Position [F2]	transmit position packet
Settings > TNC Commands > Send Objects	transmit objects packet
Settings > TNC Commands > Send Grid-Square Position	transmit Maidenhead grid square packet
Settings > TNC Commands > Send Weather Report	transmit weather report packet
Settings > TNC Commands > Send RDF Report	transmit direction finding packet
Settings > TNC Commands > Send APRS Query	transmit APRS station query packet
Settings > TNC Commands > Send WX Query	transmit an APRS weather station query packet
Settings > TNC Commands > Send IGate Query	transmit APRS IGate station query packet
Settings > TNC Commands > VHF-Reinitialize TNC	configure VHF/UHF TNC with TNC Settings parameters
Settings > TNC Commands > VHF-Exit KISS Mode	force VHF/UHF TNC to quit KISS mode
Settings > TNC Commands > VHF-Exit Kantronics Host Mode	force VHF/UHF TNC to quit Kantronics TNC host mode
Settings > TNC Commands > VHF-Exit AEA Host Mode	force VHF/UHF TNC to quit AEA TNC host mode
Settings > TNC Commands > HF-Reinitialize TNC	configure HF TNC with TNC Settings parameters
Settings > TNC Commands > HF-Exit KISS Mode	force HF TNC to quit KISS mode

Settings > TNC Commands > HF-Exit Kantronics Host Mode	force HF TNC to quit Kantronics TNC host mode
Settings > TNC Commands > HF-Exit AEA Host Mode	force HF TNC to quit AEA TNC host mode
Settings > TNC Commands > Alternate VHF Path > -None-	configure no Unproto VHF/UHF path
Settings > TNC Commands > Alternate VHF Path > Default	configure Unproto VHF/UHF path with default path
Settings > TNC Commands > Alternate VHF Path > Other...	configure Unproto VHF/UHF path with user-defined path
Settings > TNC Commands > Alternate VHF Path > relay,WIDE	configure Unproto VHF/UHF path as RELAY, WIDE
Settings > TNC Commands > Alternate VHF Path > WIDE,WIDE	configure Unproto VHF/UHF path as WIDE,WIDE
Settings > TNC Commands > Alternate VHF Path > WIDE,GATE	configure Unproto VHF/UHF path as WIDE,GATE
Settings > TNC Commands > Alternate VHF Path > WIDE-3	configure Unproto VHF/UHF path as WIDE-3
Settings > TNC Commands > Alternate HF Path > -None-	configure no Unproto HF path
Settings > TNC Commands > Alternate HF Path > Default	configure Unproto HF path with default path
Settings > TNC Commands > Alternate HF Path > Other...	configure Unproto HF path with user-defined path
Settings > TNC Commands > Alternate HF Path > relay,WIDE	configure Unproto HF path as RELAY,WIDE
Settings > TNC Commands > Alternate HF Path > WIDE,WIDE	configure Unproto HF path as WIDE,WIDE
Settings > TNC Commands > Alternate HF Path > WIDE,GATE	configure Unproto HF path as WIDE,GATE
Settings > TNC Commands > Alternate HF Path > WIDE-3	configure Unproto HF path as WIDE-3
Settings > TNC Commands > TCP/IP Connections > TCP Server Settings	configure options regarding APRServer connections
Settings > TNC Commands > TCP/IP Connections > Show TCP Status Log	display information regarding APRServer connection
Settings > TNC Commands > TCP/IP Connections > Close All TCP Ports	disconnect from all APRServer

Command	Description
Settings > TNC Commands > TCP/IP Connections > Connect To APRServe Network	connect to APRServer network
Settings > TNC Commands > TCP/IP Connections > (server names)	connect to selected APRServer from list
Settings > TNC Commands > Send Position [F2]	transmit position packet
Settings > TNC Commands > Send Query	transmit APRS query packet
Settings > TNC Commands > Send Weather	transmit weather report packet
Settings > TNC Commands > Send WX Query	transmit an APRS weather station query packet
Logging > Station Logging	turn on/off recording received station data
Logging > WinAPRS Logging	turn on/off recording received APRS data
Logging > NMEA Logging	turn on/off recording received NMEA/GPS data
Logging > Local Weather Logging	turn on/off recording local weather reports
Logging > Message Logging	turn on/off recording received messages
Logging > Local RDF Logging	turn on/off recording local direction finding data
Logging > Stop All Logging	disable recording all received data
Maps > Display Map Boundaries [B]	display perimeters of available maps
Maps > Map List Window	display all selectable maps
Maps > (map names)	display selected map from list
Display > Home View [H]	display current map in its default size
Display > Auto Refresh Maps	turn on/off automatic map refreshing function
Display > Auto Scroll Moving Maps	turn on/off automatic scrolling map function
Display > Station Call Signs	turn on/off display of received station call signs on map
Display > Station Icons	turn on/off display of received station icons on map

GLOSSARY

American National Standard Code for Information Interchange
 (ASCII)—a seven bit digital code used in computer and
 radioteleprinter applications
AO16APRS—an email list sponsored by TAPR that is devoted to
 the discussion of using APRS with Amateur adio satellites.
APRS—abbreviation for Automatic Position Reporting System
APRS (DOS)—the original version of APRS; it runs on a *DOS*
 platform.
APRS/CE—a version of APRS that runs on *Windows CE*
 platforms.
APRS+SA—a version of APRS that runs on a *Windows* platform
 using maps running concurrently on DeLorme Street Atlas
 software.
APRServer—an Internet site that collects data from IGates to
 permit the viewing of worldwide APRS activity via the
 Internet.
APRSFD—an email list sponsored by TAPR that is intended for
 the discussion of using APRS in conjunction with Field
 Day operations.
APRSNEWS—an email list sponsored by TAPR that provides for
 the distribution of APRS news concerning new releases of
 software.
APRSSIG—an email list sponsored by TAPR that is intended for
 the discussion of all APRS topics.
APRSSPEC—an email list sponsored by TAPR that is intended
 for the discussion of the APRS protocol documentation
 project.

ASCII—abbreviation for American National Standard Code for Information Interchange

asynchronous—a data transmission timing technique that adds extra bits of information to indicate the beginning and end of each transmitted character

audio-frequency-shift keying (AFSK)—a method of transmitting digital information by switching between two audio tones fed into the transmitter audio input

Automatic Position Reporting System (APRS)—a packet radio application for tracking real-time events by graphically displaying information on maps displayed on the user's computer screen

baud—a unit of signaling speed equal to one pulse (event or symbol) per second in a single-channel transmission

beacon—a TNC function that permits a station to automatically send unconnected packets at regular intervals

bit—binary digit, a signal that is either on/one or off/zero; bits are combined to represent alphanumeric and control characters for data communications

BText—the TNC command that configures the contents of a packet radio beacon.

byte—a group of bits, usually eight in number

CGA—abbreviation for color graphics adapter.

Clear To Send (CTS)—an EIA-232 serial interface signal, which informs the DTE when the DCE is ready to transmit data.

color graphics adapter (CGA)—a computer monitor type or standard

CTS—abbreviation for Clear To Send.

data circuit-terminating equipment, data communications equipment (DCE)—the device that provides communications between a DTE and radio equipment or telephone lines

data terminal equipment (DTE)—a device that is used as an interface between a human and a computer to allow the human to exchange information with the computer

Data Terminal Ready (DTR)—an EIA-232 serial interface signal, which informs the DCE when the DTE is ready for data communications.

DB-25—a connector that transfers 25 signals, typically used for computer serial port connections.

DB-9—a connector that transfers 9 signals, typically used for computer serial port connections.

DCE—abbreviation for data circuit-terminating equipment and data communications equipment

default—the state of a TNC parameter after the TNC is initially turned on or reset

deviation—in the FM mode, the amount that the carrier frequency is shifted in proportion to the amplitude of the input signal.

DF—abbreviation for direction finding

digipeater—digital repeater, a device that receives, temporarily stores and then transmits (repeats) packet radio transmissions that are specifically addressed for routing through the digipeater

direction finding (DF)—a means of locating a radio station by determining the compass bearing of the source of the radio station's signal.

Doppler—the change of frequency of a radio wave that occurs as the velocity of its source changes relative to the observer.

DTE—abbreviation for data terminal equipment.

DTR—abbreviation for Data Terminal Ready.

EGA—abbreviation for enhanced graphics adapter.

EIA—abbreviation for Electronic Industries Association

EIA-232—the EIA standard for DTE-to-DCE (TNC) interfacing that specifies the interface signals and their electrical characteristics

EIA-422—an EIA standard for DTE-to-DCE (TNC) interfacing that specifies the interface signals and their electrical characteristics.

Electronic Industries Association (EIA)—an organization composed of representatives of the United States electronics industry; the EIA is involved in formulating data communication standards.

enhanced graphics adapter (EGA)—a computer monitor type or standard.

Enter—a key on a computer keyboard that causes the computer to accept the information previously typed at its keyboard

enter—to use a key (for example, the Enter key) on a computer keyboard to cause the computer to accept the information previously typed at its keyboard

fade point—the location where a direction-finding station loses or acquires the signal transmitted by an unknown station

gateway—a device or PBBS function that allows packet radio stations on different operating frequencies to communicate with each other

Global Positioning System (GPS)—a system that uses orbiting satellites to determine the location of GPS receiving stations on the surface of the Earth

GPS—abbreviation for Global Positioning System

HAAT—abbreviation for Height Above Average Terrain.

Hardware Single Port Switch (HSP)—a circuit built into a cable that permits the connection of a GPS receiver and a TNC to the same computer serial port.

Height Above Average Terrain (HAAT)—the difference between the elevation of an antenna and the average elevation of the land area surrounding the antenna.

HotSync—the process of transferring data between a Palm III PDA and a computer.

HSP—abbreviation for Hardware Single Port Switch.

HTAPRS—an email list sponsored by TAPR that is devoted to the discussion of APRS topics related to the Kenwood TH-D7 handheld transceiver.

IGate—an APRS station connected to the Internet that relays the APRS data it receives locally to central Internet sites called APRServers.

kbyte—one thousand bytes.

Long Range Navigation (LORAN)—a radio system used by ships and planes to determine their location.

LORAN—abbreviation for Long Range Navigation.

MacAPRS—a version of Automatic Packet/Position Reporting System (APRS) that runs on a Macintosh platform

MIC—abbreviation for microphone.

MIC-E—an email list sponsored by TAPR that is intended for the discussion of the MIC-E module.

Micro Interface Module (MIM)—a telemetry TNC in one integrated circuit

MIM—abbreviation for Micro Interface Module.

---

modem—modulator-demodulator; an electronic device that permits digital equipment to use analog communications media for data communications

MYAlias—the TNC command that configures a pseudonym for the identification of a packet radio station.

MYCall—the TNC command that configures the identification of a packet radio station.

National Marine Electronics Association (NMEA)—the organization responsible for the standards used for GPS and other navigation systems.

network—a system of interconnected packet radio stations assembled for the efficient transfer of packets over long distances

NMEA—abbreviation for National Marine Electronics Association

NMEA-0183—a standard used for GPS and other navigation systems, which was developed by the National Marine Electronics Association (NMEA); it is compatible with APRS.

path—the route between two connected packet radio stations consisting of digipeaters and other packet stations

PDA—abbreviation for personal digital assistant.

PHGD—abbreviation for Power-Height-Gain-Direction.

pocketAPRS—a version of APRS that runs on the 3Com Palm III Connected Organizer, a hand-held personal digital assistant (PDA).

port—a circuit that allows a device to communicate with external devices.

posit text—a short string of text sent whenever APRS transmits a station's position packet.

position comment—a short string of text sent whenever APRS transmits a station's position packet.

position packet—an Unnumbered Information (UI) packet generated by APRS that contains information concerning the location of the APRS station; the latitude and longitude of an APRS station.

Power-Height-Gain-Direction (PHGD)—information concerning an APRS station that may be included in its APRS transmissions.

PROPNET—an email list sponsored by TAPR that is devoted to an ongoing VHF propagation experiment using APRS.

PTT—abbreviation for press-to-talk.

radio port—the TNC port that is connected to a radio transceiver (or transmitter and receiver)

RAM—abbreviation for random-access memory

random-access memory (RAM)—a data storage device that can be written to and read from

Received Data—an EIA-232 serial interface signal that consists of data from the DCE (TNC) that was received over the communication medium and demodulated by the DCE (TNC)

RELAY—an APRS digipeater that has a small coverage area; it is intended to feed its packets to WIDE digipeaters that have coverage of wide expanses of an APRS network.

RJ-45—a connector that transfers 6 signals, typically used for computer serial port connections.

Secondary Station Identifier (SSID)—a number that follows a packet radio station call sign to differentiate between two or more packet radio stations operating under the same call sign

serial port—an interconnection that transfers bit-encoded information bit-by-bit (serially); the TNC connection for a terminal or computer

Signal Ground—an EIA-232 serial interface signal that provides a common ground reference for all the other interface signals except Shield (pin 1)

SSID—abbreviation for secondary station identifier

status text—a short string of text sent whenever APRS transmits a station's beacon.

stop bit—one or two extra bits that follow a character to indicate its end in asynchronous data communications

TAPR—abbreviation for Tucson Amateur Packet Radio Corporation.

telemetry—information collected remotely that is transmitted to a distant collection site.

terminal—short for data terminal equipment or a computer emulating data terminal equipment

terminal node controller (TNC)—an Amateur Radio packet assembler/disassembler; may or may not include a modem

TNC—abbreviation for terminal-node controller

TNC 2—the second TAPR TNC that was made available to the general public; based on a Z80 microprocessor; its design was the most popular in amateur packet radio history

TRACEn-n—an APRS digipeater protocol that simplifies digipeater addressing and permits tracking the digipeater path of a packet.

Transmitted Data—an EIA-232 serial interface signal that consists of data from a DTE that is intended for transmission by the DCE (TNC) over the communication medium; also called Send Data.

Tucson Amateur Packet Radio Corporation (TAPR)—the Arizona-based Amateur Radio organization that was instrumental in packet radio protocol and hardware development in the United States.

TXdelay—the TNC command that configures the length of time inserted between the time the TNC keys a transmitter and the time the TNC sends data to the transmitter.

UI—abbreviation for Unnumbered Information frame

unconnected packets—packets transmitted from a source station with no specific destination station being addressed; used for beacons, CQs, and round table communications

United States Geological Survey (USGS)—a federal agency which is a source for map data used for creating APRS maps.

Unnumbered Information (UI)—an AX.25 unnumbered frame that allows data to be transmitted from a source station with no specific destination station being addressed.

Unproto—the TNC command that determines the digipeater path of packets sent in the unconnected (unprotocol) mode.

Unprotocol—the packet radio mode in which packets are broadcasted, rather than being transmitted to a specifically addressed connected station.

USB—abbreviation for Universal Serial Bus.

USGS—abbreviation for United States Geological Survey

VGA—abbreviation for video graphics adapter.

video graphics adapter (VGA)—a computer monitor type or
   standard.

WIDE—an APRS digipeater that is well-situated in order to
   provide coverage of wide expanses of an APRS network.

WIDEn-n—an APRS digipeater protocol that simplifies digipeater
   addressing and promotes network efficiency.

WinAPRS—a version of APRS that runs on a *Windows* platform.

XAPRS—a version of APRS that runs on *Linux* platforms.

XASTIR—a version of APRS that runs on *Linux* platforms.

XOFF—transmitter off; a flow control character used in ASCII
   data transfers; it commands the transmitter to stop sending
   data.

XON—transmitter on; a flow control character used in ASCII data
   transfers; it commands the transmitter to send data.

INDEX

FEEDBACK

Please use this form to give us your comments on this book and what you'd like to see in future editions. You can also e-mail your comments to us at **pubsfdbk@arrl.org** (publications feedback). In that case, please be sure to include your name, call, e-mail address and the book title and edition in the body of your e-mail message. Also indicate whether or not you are an ARRL member.

Where did you purchase this book?
    ☐ From ARRL directly   ☐ From an ARRL dealer

Is there a dealer who carries ARRL publications within:
    ☐ 5 miles   ☐ 15 miles   ☐ 30 miles   of your location?   ☐ Not sure.

License class:
☐ Novice	☐ Technician	☐ Technician Plus
☐ General	☐ Advanced	☐ Extra

Name _____

ARRL member? ☐ Yes ☐ No

_____ Call Sign _____

Daytime Phone ( ) _____ Age _____

Address _____ E-mail address _____

City, State/Province, ZIP/Postal Code _____

If licensed, how long? _____

Other hobbies _____

Occupation _____

From _____

_____

_____

EDITOR, APRS-2
ARRL
225 MAIN STREET
NEWINGTON CT 06111-1494

.... please fold and tape ....